THEMES IN CANADIAN LITERATURE
General Editor *David Arnason*

The Urban Experience

Edited by
John Stevens

Macmillan of Canada

© 1975 The Macmillan Company of Canada Limited
70 Bond Street, Toronto M5B 1X3
Affiliated with Maclean-Hunter Learning Materials Company.

ISBN 0-7705-1267-4

Themes in Canadian Literature

The Urban Experience edited by John Stevens
The Maritime Experience edited by Michael O. Nowlan
The Frontier Experience edited by Jack Hodgins
The Prairie Experience edited by Terry Angus
Isolation in Canadian Literature edited by David Arnason and
    Alice K. Hale
The Immigrant Experience edited by Leuba Bailey
Native Peoples in Canadian Literature edited by William and
    Christine Mowat
The Artist in Canadian Literature edited by Lionel Wilson
The Search for Identity edited by James Foley
The Role of Woman in Canadian Literature edited by Elizabeth
    McCullough
Canadian Humour and Satire edited by Theresa Ford

Other titles in preparation

Printed in Canada

ACKNOWLEDGMENTS

Permission to reprint the following copyright material is gratefully acknowledged.

Photographs: p. 19, Ontario Ministry of Industry & Tourism; p. 34, Province of Quebec Film Bureau; p. 37, Miller Services Ltd.; p. 45, Joan Latchford; p. 51, Ontario Ministry of Industry & Tourism; p. 75, Miller Services Ltd.; p. 86, Ontario Ministry of Industry & Tourism; p. 102, Ontario Ministry of Industry & Tourism; p. 105, *Vancouver Sun.*

Milton Acorn: "On Saint-Urbain Street" from *I've Tasted My Blood* by Milton Acorn, The Ryerson Press (1969).
Margaret Atwood: "They Eat Out" from *Power Politics,* © 1971 by Margaret Atwood, reprinted by permission of House of Anansi Press Limited.
Earle Birney: "i think you are a whole city" from *Collected Poems of Earle Birney*, reprinted by permission of McClelland and Stewart Limited, Toronto.
Frank Davey: "Vancouver I" from *Bridge Force* by Frank Davey, reprinted by permission of the Author.
Louis Dudek: "Tree in a Street" from *Collected Poetry* by Louis Dudek, Delta Canada (1971), reprinted by permission of the Author.
Hugh Garner: "The Happiest Man in the World" © 1971 by Hugh Garner, from *Fourteen Stories High* edited by David Helwig and Tom Marshall, reprinted by permission of the Author.
James H. Gray: "The Saga of the Fine-toothed Comb" from *The Boy From Winnipeg* by James H. Gray, reprinted by permission of The Macmillan Company of Canada Limited.
Lawren Harris: "Greetings" from *Contrasts* by Lawren Harris, reprinted by permission of Lawren Harris Estate.
Hugh Hood: "Flying a Red Kite" from *Flying a Red Kite* by Hugh Hood, reprinted by permission of McGraw-Hill Ryerson Limited.
Lionel Kearns: "The Birth of God" from *By the Light of the Silvery McLune, Media Parables, Poems, Signs, Gestures, and Other Assaults on the Interface* by Lionel Kearns, Talon books (1969), reprinted by permission of the Author.
A. M. Klein: "Autobiographical" from *The Second Scroll* by A. M. Klein, copyright 1951 by A. M. Klein. Reprinted by permission of Alfred A. Knopf, Inc.
Archibald Lampman: "The City of the End of Things" from *The Poems of Archibald Lampman*, edited by Duncan Campbell Scott (1900).
Stephen Leacock: "My Friend the Reporter" from *Short Circuits* by Stephen Leacock, reprinted by permission of McClelland and Stewart Limited.

CONTENTS

INTRODUCTION: THE URBAN MAGNET

In 1861 a Scottish settler in Upper Canada published a long poem called *The Emigrant*. At one point in the narrative the chief character and his companions, all newly arrived in Canada and travelling the wilderness to their homesteads, pause to make camp for the night. Before sleeping they gather under a birch tree to carol their praises of the Canadian greenwood and to express their hatred for the city slums of the Old World left behind. (See page 46.) The author of the poem, Alexander McLachlan, was typical of early writers in making his characters thus rhapsodize over the rural beauties of Canada. But, in fact, the writers themselves often gravitated away from the scenic charms they praised toward such urban centres as then existed. A somewhat earlier writer, Mrs. Susanna Moodie, confesses at the end of *Roughing It in the Bush* with what relief she sold the family farm and left "the prison house" of the Upper Canada backwoods to live in the "busy town" of Belleville. And even Alexander McLachlan, whose poems continued to exalt country living, spent frequent sojourns in town.

Throughout the nineteenth century and for the first decade of the twentieth, government grants of farmland attracted many thousands of immigrants to Canada— in the early years to Ontario and Quebec and then, with the completion of the Canadian Pacific Railway, to the prairies and beyond. Between 1901 and 1911 half a million newcomers passed through Winnipeg alone, most of them bound for a new life as prairie farmers. But in the 1920s, as industrialization increased, the children of these immigrants thronged into the cities. The prolonged industrial boom following the Second World War accelerated this shift of population so that in the present decade four out of five Canadians live in an urban environment, with more than half of Canada's total population concentrated in the seventeen largest metropolitan areas.

Canadian literature has recorded this flight from rural settlement. In many novels chronicling the lives of rural dwellers the central character either leaves for the city or at least has a strong urge to do so. Hagar Shipley in *The Stone Angel*, the Bentleys in *As for Me and My House*, and Gander Stakes in *Grain* spring to mind as obvious examples. However, city life solves few personal problems. The Mercer family in David French's recent play, *Leaving*

1

Home, breaks up after its members have moved from their small Newfoundland community to Toronto. Certainly the diverse voices that we hear in the poetry and prose of *The Urban Experience* tell us how different is the real city from the New Jerusalem of pilgrims' hopes. Admittedly, a crowded metropolis can provide abundant goods and services and a sophisticated network of communications, but it also breeds crime, loneliness, the aggressive pursuit of material success, and the ultimate breakdown of real communication between people.

All the conditions above find expression in this anthology. The loneliness of old age and the violence of youth meet in the fog of Ethel Wilson's Vancouver story. Loneliness and a sense of the dream lost in competitive turmoil are evident in the stories "The Happiest Man in the World" and "Flying a Red Kite", as they are in the poems "The Stenographers" and "Warren Pryor". Indeed, P. K. Page's stenographers and Alden Nowlan's bank teller seem to live their barren lives at the very gates of the nightmare city envisaged in Archibald Lampman's "The City of the End of Things".

However, not all is lamentation. From the nettle of drought and depression Ken Mitchell plucks the flower of laughter in "The Great Electrical Revolution". And Stephen Leacock in his light-hearted sketch from the 1920s reminds us that municipal graft and the distortion of news by the big city dailies have their funny side, too. A. M. Klein celebrates the ghetto streets of his Montreal childhood, made fabulous by memory; Earle Birney creates a whole city out of wit and words to do homage to the beauty of his beloved; F. R. Scott turns suburban aloofness into a matter for satiric mockery, and Margaret Atwood sends up her theme of sexual love-hatred to a comic climax as her lover-enemy rises from their restaurant table to soar over the neon town, an absurd superman with synchronized flashing eyes.

The view offered by this sampling of Canadian urban writing suggests that although the maple-leafed city may be sometimes a place for bitter regrets and sometimes a place for satiric laughter, one thing is certain: it is never merely dull.

John Stevens

THE HAPPIEST MAN IN THE WORLD
Hugh Garner

It had been a typical Friday afternoon at the office, with no hint of what was to come. When he got the news it came to him without warning, as promotions always did at Cambrian Trust.

He'd finished cleaning up his work, locking all his files away except the Routledge portfolio; that he intended to prepare, over the weekend, for the legal department. He'd placed the file in his Slimline attaché case lying open on his desk, and had glanced at his watch. It was 5:35. As usual he was the last of the estate adjustors still in the office.

He'd pulled on his topcoat when Mr. Wilburt, the department head, tapped on the glass of his corner office and with a beckoning finger had summoned him. He'd nodded, picked up his attaché case and hat, and made his way between the empty desks to T.C.'s office.

Without asking him to sit down the older man had raised his balding grey head and asked, "How old are you now?"

"Thirty-eight, sir."

"And you've been with us how long?"

"Ten years. Seven of them as an adjustor."

"I was an adjustor fifteen years," Wilburt said gruffly. "I may as well tell you that it was a toss-up between you and — well, somebody else. Some of us thought you were still a little young for it, but your work record and the business administration degree you received through extension courses — what's that, night school?" Ed nodded. "Those things made us decide you were the man." The department manager tilted his chair back and said with a slight smile, "Well, Eddy, I guess you're it."

"I'm it?" he'd asked, keeping the sudden flurry beneath his ribs from showing in his question.

"It was all settled this afternoon up in Stan Parker's office," Wilburt said, welcoming him into the Cambrian management team by calling the president by his first name. "I'm leaving at the end of next week for my place at Vero Beach to spend the winter surf-casting. You'll move in here on Monday morning, but I'll be hovering over your shoulder for a couple of days to fill you in on procedures, and work you into the routine."

"You're leaving us for good?" Ed asked, not letting on that the old man's coming retirement had been office gossip for months.

"Yes. I've reached the mandatory age, and my wife Ellen and I have had this little place down in Florida for years. It's been generally boarded up except for a month every winter, or when the kids and their families have used it. We haven't made up our minds yet whether to sell the house up here and move down there permanently or not."

"I'm sorry to see you go, Mr. Wilburt," he'd said, not quite truthfully. Then had added, "After forty years you deserve it, sir."

The old man had laughed, nodding to himself in agreement. "Call me Tom, Eddy. See you Monday morning, when we'll go up to Stan's office to finalize the deal."

"You bet—Tom. And thanks. Thank you very much."

The old man had bent over the papers on his desk and dismissed him with an offhanded wave.

As Ed Grogan stepped from the elevator into the underground car-park of the tall office building he glanced across at his car. His four-year-old black Pontiac suddenly looked shabby standing there in the almost empty garage, but as he walked toward it he thought happily that now he'd be able to trade up to something bigger. Nothing too ostentatious, of course, for the short suburban street in Greenbriar Hills, but something just a little better. There was no doubt in his mind that Jennifer would have her say about spending his salary increase, but she surely wouldn't object to a new car, or to them joining the Greenbriar golf club. Most of her friends belonged to it, and it would put an end to him having to line up at the tees, with Gord Monroe, at the municipal course in the summer. He remembered the speaker at the Jaycees dinner who had said, "Happiness is success." Tonight Ed Grogan was the happiest man in the world.

He smiled and nodded to the uniformed watchman as he drove out of the garage, and found himself having to curb a joyful urge to hit the gas just a little harder as he turned along the downtown street. Some of them thought him "square", and maybe he was, but the years of hard work, study, and attention to detail had paid off after all. He eased his foot on the gas pedal; he couldn't let his euphoria blow everything for him now.

He thought of the others in the office, some of whom would be drinking now in the Paradise Room, as they did every Friday evening. The Paradise Room had been just one of the things he'd had to sacrifice over the years, in order to continue his schooling, to placate Jennifer, and to get ahead. He wondered if any of the others from the office had ever realized there'd been times, many times, when he'd envied them. He'd never really learned to drink, or like it, but mixing with the others at the Paradise might have eased his loneliness, and shown them what he was *really* like.

The traffic on the parkway had passed its rush-hour peak, and Ed kept his speed just under five miles above the limit, watching out for both Friday-night drunks and the unmarked police cars that patrolled the road. He stuck to the middle traffic lane, letting those in a hurry pass by on the left, while avoiding the right-hand lane with its slower traffic turning off at the exit ramps.

He tried to keep his exultation in check but his thoughts remained on what this promotion meant to him, and especially to Jennifer. Now she'd be able to have a woman come in one day a week, just like the Bracketts. After all, Carl Brackett was only a sales supervisor for an air-conditioning firm, and according to street gossip the Bracketts were in debt up to their eyeballs.

Greenbriar Hills was only a fifteen-minute run up the parkway, now almost a part of the city to those who lived in the newer subdivisions farther out. Ten years ago, when he'd bought his new home there before the parkway was finished, it had taken him three-quarters of an hour to get downtown. As one of the then-new outer suburbs, it had been called by its developers "The in-place for young families on their way up".

Ten years ago, of course, he hadn't really been on his way anywhere, with his dead-end job in the railroad freight office. Then everything had happened at once. He'd met Jennifer, who was "in social service work", when she was on the re-bound from a broken courtship. She'd been aggressively ardent in those days, and they'd been forced into a hasty marriage. His mother had passed away, leaving him just enough money to put a down payment on the house, and furnish it.

It had been Jenny (as she'd let him call her then), through vague connections, who had secured him the interview and the subsequent job at the trust company. It was true, as they said, that behind every successful man was an ambitious wife.

For one exhilarating moment he wondered if his new job would help him convince Jennifer they should have another baby. It wasn't healthy for young Colin to be an only child. Up to now she had countered his hints with the excuse that they couldn't afford another baby just yet. Several of her women friends had only one child too, a token claim to womanhood, but one that least restricted them socially.

He turned off the parkway at the Greenbriar cloverleaf, and at the posted residential speed limit followed the winding streets to his house. The rollaway garage door beneath the window of the master bedroom was open, though he'd com-plained to Jennifer and ten-year-old Colin to keep it closed so that the smaller children on the street wouldn't take things from his workbench or spill his paint. Since Jennifer's last asth-matic attack over a year ago he had been relegated to the smaller bedroom next to Colin's.

After locking the car in the garage he entered the house through the connecting door and shouted from the kitchen, "Jennifer, I'm home!"

"Your supper's in the oven," came her flat reply from the living-room. "You're late. Colin and I couldn't wait." It was a habit of hers to tack an admonitory ending to almost every answer she gave him, but after ten years he hardly noticed it.

He opened the oven door and took out a lukewarm dish containing the remains of a tuna casserole. Jennifer must have been playing bridge all afternoon, or shopping again with Elsa DeBrough, a friend who was a sort of amateur sculptor and home decorator.

As he took a plate and cup and saucer from a cupboard he thought nostalgically of the family dishes his mother had served: short ribs, beef stews, even shepherd's pie. The teapot was cold, so he filled the kettle and brewed himself a fresh pot of tea. Jennifer and Colin must have had an early supper for things to have grown as cold as they were. The frenetic sounds of a family comedy show came from the TV set in the living-room.

After he had eaten, the glow of happiness over his promotion came back to him, and he took a cigar from a half-empty box he had received from the firm last Christmas, and lighted it. Clenching it between his teeth he tried to act out a young-executive fantasy as he washed up the supper things, including the casserole dish. Then he headed for the living-room.

Jennifer, wearing a quilted housecoat, her hair freshly done in an upswept style, reclined on the sofa. Her eyes remained fixed on the television tube and her mouth was set in the half-smile she always wore when watching a favourite show. Colin lolled in a chair with his long legs climbing up its back, a bored expression on his face. He didn't look up when his father entered the room.

When a commercial interrupted the program Jennifer looked up and said, "Hi, dear. Have a good day?"

"A great one," he said, exhaling a cloud of cigar smoke as he sat down in an empty chair.

"Dear, I've asked you not to smoke those things in here,"

his wife said, curling her lip. "I've had such a day, traipsing all over town with Elsa."

"Your new hairdo looks fine, though I think I like it better when you wear it long."

"Oh, Edward . . . " she said, with an exasperated little laugh.

"How've you been, Colin?" he asked.

"All right," the boy answered, without looking up.

"Sssh!" she cautioned as the program returned to the screen.

After a brief glance at the show he looked over at his wife. For some reason she reminded him of the asexual slim thirtyish models who advertised nail polish, profile pointed away from the camera, her manicured fingers displayed in her lap. Jennifer's looks *were* those of a modish middle-class executive's wife, he thought happily. When they occasionally attended functions together he was proud to introduce her, stretching himself as tall as he could to equal their heights.

He took his cigar into the hallway, and picked up his mail from the antique table the DeBrough woman had palmed off on them. He shuffled it through his hands: the electric bill, an announcement from Rotary, a charitable request from his church, the monthly statement from Group Investors Inc., a letter bearing the postmark of the town where his sister Norma lived, and a mauve envelope that Jennifer must have opened by mistake. He took a typewritten mauve sheet from the opened envelope and glanced at the signature. Karen Grierson. He read the note, a request for a job recommendation. Now he remembered who Karen Grierson was, a young typist who had taken the place of Mrs. Cluff, down at the office, the summer before.

He smiled warmly to himself at the memory of the girl. She'd been a crazily alive little thing who said things like, "I dig," and, "Shall I stash this in the files, Mr. Grogan?" He carried the letter into the kitchen and put it in an inside pocket of his suit coat. He was touched that she'd requested a recommendation from *him*.

Carrying the rest of the letters in his hand he returned to the living-room just as Jennifer's comedy show came to an end.

"Your friends the Bracketts are moving," his wife said. They'd been "your friends" to her since the Sunday afternoon he'd crossed the street to give Carl Brackett a hand with a small auto-repair job. He'd stayed and had a couple of cold beers with Carl and his wife in their kitchen.

"They're moving! Where to?"

"A downtown apartment, I hear. I guess their debts have finally caught up with them."

He glanced quickly at young Colin. "I don't think it's that, Jennifer."

"*You* can stick up for them if you like." She wafted some imaginary cigar smoke away from her face. Colin uncoiled himself from the chair and left the room.

Ed said, "It finally happened, Jennifer. I'm taking over Wilburt's desk on Monday."

She sat up straight and smiled. "So he's retiring? It's about time." She crossed the floor and placed her arms dutifully around his neck. "I'm pleased, Edward. I'm glad you beat out Thompson and that icky old Peterson."

He circled her with his arm. Until then he hadn't thought of the promotion as being a contest between himself and the other adjustors, but now he suddenly realized that Peterson and Thompson both had more seniority than he. The realization appalled him.

Being careful of her hairdo she brushed his cheek with her lips, but when he pushed himself to his feet and tried to kiss her she drew herself away with a practised twist. "Not now, dear . . . Colin's here . . . ," she whispered. She left the room, smiling over her shoulder. He sat down again and opened his sister's letter.

It was the usual summary of the month's events relating to herself, her druggist husband, and her two pretty daughters. As he read her misspelled scrawl he felt a warm family feeling creep over him, and he made up his mind to visit them around Christmas, whether Jennifer came or not.

He carried the rest of the mail into his den, where he wrote out a couple of cheques and filed the investment statement. He caught a whiff of Jennifer's expensive perfume on himself, and smiled at the promise implied in her words, "Not now, dear...."

A little later Jennifer came to the door and said, "Edward, I think we should have a few friends drop in tomorrow evening to celebrate, don't you?"

"Yes. That'll be fine, dear."

"It won't be a regular party or anything like that. Just the DeBroughs, Hamiltons, Sylvia and Merv Appel, and the new member of the bridge club, Bette Parks, and her husband."

"How about Gord and Edna Monroe? After all we owe them an invite after them taking us to the club dance in September."

"Not this time, dear. You know how Gordon Monroe drinks."

She had a legitimate point there. "All right, I'll leave it to you," he said.

"And, Edward, I'm out of cigarettes. Would you drive over to the plaza and pick me up a pack?"

"While I'm there I may as well get a couple of bottles of Scotch too," he said.

"Don't forget Elsa drinks nothing but gin."

"We have gin."

"Colin wants to go to one of the stores in the plaza too. While you're gone I'll phone everybody."

Driving over to the shopping plaza Ed tried to draw his son out on the subject of his school work, but the boy answered him in monosyllables. When he parked in an empty parking space in front of the liquor store Colin jumped out, saying he was going to pick up some tubes of paint at the hobby shop. Ed was proud of his son's ability as a painter; even his school-teacher had written Jennifer praising the boy's work.

10

He ran into Carl and Grace Brackett outside the liquor store, and they exchanged pleasantries on the sidewalk. They didn't mention their moving, so he didn't bring it up. Both invited him over to their house later for a drink, but he excused himself. "I'm getting some Scotch for tomorrow night," he told them. "Jennifer is having some of her friends drop in."

"That'll be nice," Grace said.

Carl Brackett pretended to let his bag of liquor slip from his hands, and Grace berated him. "Brackett, you drop that and it's the divorce court for you!" They all laughed.

Ed watched the Bracketts heading for the supermarket, both wearing old sweaters and slacks, bumping each other with their hips as they walked, and laughing. He envied them the fun they seemed to get out of living.

When he came out of the liquor store he helped a shabby man open his car door, and watched smiling as four or five children piled into the old second-hand car, their harassed father struggling with two big bags of groceries. It reminded him of the gypsy-like families he and Jennifer had passed on the highways on their trip once to Yellowstone; second-hand station wagons and old pick-up trucks piled with camping paraphernalia and kids. For just a fleeting moment he felt he had lost something from life.

When the man with the children vacated the parking space next to his, Ed sat in his car waiting for Colin to return from the hobby shop. A white convertible with the top up, and two men in the front seat, pulled past the empty space, then began backing into it. Ed saw that they weren't going to make it, and he blew a warning on his horn. The driver ignored it, and there was a rather heavy bump on one front corner of his car, followed by a scraping sound. The convertible completed its reversing into the space, and straightened out about a foot away from Ed's car. He had to slide across the front seat to get out through the right-hand door.

He walked to the front of his car, and looked down to see what damage had been done. It seemed that only his front bumper had been bent slightly out of line. The convertible, however, had a long indentation along its front fender and door. Both its occupants climbed out of the driver's side and came around to where Ed was standing.

"You don't seem to have done any damage to me," Ed said. "I blew my horn to warn you that you were turning too tight."

The men ignored him, and stood staring at the long, ugly scar that ran along the convertible's white-painted side. One of them, a pot-bellied man wearing a purple-and-yellow hockey club windbreaker, its sleeves and front decorated with adolescent crests and badges, said, "You'll pay for this, mister."

"What!"

"You heard me," the man said. Ed noticed that he was about his own age but a little taller. "Look where you're parked," the man snarled, "nearly over the white dividing line an' at least a foot too far forward."

Ed looked. His car *was* up against the white line, but not across it. He'd been forced to crowd over to the left by a big car parked on the other side of him, that had now gone. "I'm still parked on my side of the line," he said quietly.

"A smart guy eh? One a these Greenbriar Hills punks thinks he owns everything around here, eh?"

Ed noticed now that the man was drunk, weaving on his feet as he shoved his face forward belligerently. A small group of shoppers, arms loaded with paper bags, began to gather in a wide semi-circle around them. Some teen-agers drifted over from where they'd been lounging in front of a hamburger bar. "Give 'im a rap on the mouth!" a thin, string-haired girl screamed shrilly. Her companions began to goad the drunk.

The man in the windbreaker looked around, saw the crowd, and said, "'at's what I should do, give 'im a rap in the mouth." He turned to his companion, a tall sober-looking man wearing a dress shirt and tie covered by a cardigan. "Waddya think, Walt?"

"Take it easy, Johnny," his friend said.

12

The drunk turned to Ed. "Walt here's a lawyer, an' he'll tell ya we can sue. Take this guy's licence, Walt, an' see if he's got insur'nce."

The reference to insurance angered Ed more than anything else. Did this drunken lout think he would drive without being fully covered against accidents? "We'll get a policeman," he said. "I don't show my licence to anyone else."

"Fuzz lover!" screeched the teen-age virago, while her companions heckled him.

"Waddya mean, cop?" the drunk asked, breaking from his friend's grasp and reaching for Ed's lapels. Ed backed away, bringing derisive jeers from the young punks. The drunk, encouraged by the falsetto shouts of his long-haired claque, gave Ed a short jab to the nose, jolting him back against his car.

The unexpected blow surprised Ed, but he was more surprised to find that his nose was bleeding, a rivulet of blood running down across his lips. Through his watering eyes he saw the pot-bellied man drawing his fist back to hit him again, and in a mixture of fear and rage he raised his arms and stumbled forward, swinging wildly. One of his fists connected with something sharp, and when he stumbled on something and opened his eyes he looked down and saw the drunk pushing himself to his knees and shaking his head. The man's bridgework jutted horribly from between his lips.

The man's tall friend helped him to his feet, and hustled him away through the crowd, as the teen-agers quickly switched their partisanship to the winner, and began a raucous mocking chant as they followed the two departing men. The crowd now broke up, the noise it was making coming from a long distance in pulsating waves. Ed took a handkerchief from his pocket and pressed it over his nose and mouth, holding on to the hood of the car as his legs began to tremble. He got into the car again, and pushed himself along the seat to the driver's side.

Now that it was over he felt a strange mixture of disgust and elation, something he couldn't remember ever having felt before. He dabbed at his nose until the bleeding stopped. When he looked down he noticed that the blood had run off his chin on to his shirt and tie, and there were a few spots on the lapels of his suit.

He hadn't noticed Colin getting into the car, but the boy was sitting beside him now, a fancy paper bag clutched on his knees. Ed hurriedly shoved his bloodied handkerchief into his pocket, and keeping his face averted asked the boy, "Are those your paints?"

"Yes."

"Good."

With the nervous care of a learning driver he slowly eased the car out of its parking space, joined a short line of cars at the exit from the parking lot, and when his turn came swung carefully into the street and drove toward home.

"Who was the man you beat up, Dad?" Colin asked him.

"I don't know. A silly man who scraped the side of his car when he was backing in next to me."

"A kid told me he used to be a hockey player. I guess they're not so tough, eh?"

"Oh, hockey players are pretty tough; they have to be. It's a rough sport. Maybe he wasn't much of a hockey player."

"*You* knocked him down."

"I was just lucky, I guess. Two grown men fighting like that is crazy."

"You broke his false teeth, Dad. You gave him three or four good ones before he even knew what happened."

"Did I? It was because I was scared I guess."

"You weren't scared. You must have been tough before you — when you were young, eh?"

"No, Skip," he said, giving the boy back a nickname that his wife had discouraged years before. "That was the first time I hit anyone since leaving school." He ruffled Colin's hair. "It's better not to fight."

"Not all the time," the boy said.

14

He smiled down at his son, and caught the boy's admiring glance, for the first time that he remembered.

As soon as he pulled into the garage Colin ran into the house. Ed locked the garage door, and followed the boy, the package of liquor held in his arm. Jennifer was waiting for him in the kitchen, and he knew from her expression that Colin had already told her about the fight. She said nothing, her eyes flashing with a cold loathing.

He stared critically at his face in a small kitchen mirror. His nose was slightly swollen, and there was dried blood on his mouth and chin and where he had wiped it across one of his cheeks. His shirt collar and necktie were a mess. He placed the liquor on the table, and walked to the short flight of back stairs leading to the upper level of the house and the bathroom.

"How could you!" Jennifer spat out. "How could you make a public spectacle of yourself right up here in the Greenbriar Plaza?"

He turned and stared at her wearily.

"In front of your own son, and — and — God knows who else!"

He stared at her as if seeing her for the first time.

"You could have been arrested! Tonight of all nights!" She whimpered in self-sympathy. "I've already called the Parks, the Appels and Hamiltons, and Elsa — "

He turned away from her, cutting off her whimpering words with the total unexpectedness of his action. As he stepped on the first stair she screamed, "Where's my cigarettes?"

He faced her again and said quietly, "I'm sorry; I forgot them." Then he took the car keys from his pocket and laid them on the sink counter. "You'll have to get them yourself," he said.

She stared at the keys, then took a couple of steps toward the stairs and shouted triumphantly, "Some drunken woman called you on the phone. She sounded as if she was in a bar."

He shrugged and made his way upstairs.

In the bathroom he took off his jacket, shirt, and tie, and washed the dried blood from his face and neck. Then he bent over the wash-basin and laved his nose with cold water. It felt tender beneath his fingers, but it wasn't broken.

Carrying the clothes he had removed, he went along the hallway to his own room. As he passed Colin's open door he glanced in at his son, who was sitting on the edge of his bed with his new tubes of paint in his hand. The boy looked up at him with a shy smile, and Ed said, "Take it easy, Skip," and winked.

In his room he took everything from the pockets of his suit, and laid the items on the dresser, throwing the suit into a corner along with his soiled shirt and tie. He pulled on a faded blue sweat shirt, threaded his belt through the loops of a pair of slacks, and pulled them on. He methodically placed the items he had taken from his suit pants into the pockets of his slacks, picking up young Karen Grierson's letter and smiling at it before transferring it to a rear pocket. After combing his hair he went downstairs to the living-room, and threw himself into a chair.

The ringing of the telephone startled him, and he heard Jennifer answer it on the kitchen extension. "It's for you!" she shouted.

Picking up the hall phone he said, "Hello. Ed Grogan here." He knew Jennifer was listening in the kitchen.

A shrill drunken woman's voice croaked, "Congratulations, Grogan, you little louse." From behind the voice he could hear conversation, the clink of glasses, and the sound of a musical combo. "What's a matter, Grogan, you got nothing to say?"

The voice was too young to belong to either Mrs. Peterson or Mrs. Thompson, even if they had been the kind of women who would call him like that.

More shrilly now, the voice said, "The whole estate

department's against you, Grogan, even old man Wilburt! Don't think you're — "

"Whose wife or mistress are you?" Ed asked gently. When there was no answer he asked, "Where are you, down at the Paradise Room?"

There was a hurried click at the end of the line, followed by that of the kitchen extension. He remained sitting at the telephone table, marvelling sadly at the universal meanness shared by all the frightened, frustrated people in the world. In a moment he heard the garage door being rolled up, and the sound of his car being backed down the driveway.

He pulled young Karen's folded mauve letter from his back pocket and read it again, letting the young girl's friendliness drive the hurt and sadness from his mind. When he returned it to his pocket, the sadness remained, but it was eased now by the knowledge that his son had learned to respect him, if for reasons he had never dreamed of until that night.

He had acted tough toward the guy in the plaza out of fright, and to the harpy on the telephone out of anger, but neither of these incidents were indicative of change. Things had gone on too long as they had been to be changed. To become something he wasn't, now, would need a complete change of personality. He might be a square, and his values might be wrong to some people, but these were things that had become part of him over his thirty-eight years, and it was too late to change them now. Even if he wished to. He sighed.

When the phone rang again he stepped into the hall and jerked the receiver from its cradle, shouting, "Hello!"

A man's laughing voice said, "Take it easy, killer. It's Carl."

"Carl Brackett?" Ed laughed with relief. "I'm sorry, Carl, I was expecting a different kind of call."

"Grace and I saw you flatten that professional Frank Merriwell in the plaza. It's about time somebody took that Little League jerk outa the playoffs."

"It was a fluke, Carl. Believe me, I didn't want — "

"Just a minute, Grace wants to talk to you."

"Hi, Ed. Listen, if you need a couple of witnesses or any-thing, Carl and I saw the whole thing. I decided old butter-fingers here should put the bottled goods in the car before we went over to the supermarket, so that's how we saw what hap-pened. How about you and your wife dropping over for a drinky-poo, as the crazy broad next door to us always calls it?"

"Thanks. Jennifer's gone over for some cigarettes, but I'll ask her when she comes back. I hear you two are moving off the street?"

"Boy, how the news gets around up here! Yeah we are, Ed. Now that young Alice is married and Libby's gone to nursing school we figured we'd fob off this Bauhaus Gothic on to some social upward achiever, as the psychologists call them. We're moving to a downtown apartment to ride the subway." There was the sound of a short scuffle. When Grace returned to the line she said, "I just stole Carl's drink; he was already one up on me. Come on over if you can, Ed. We'd love to have you."

Ed hung up the phone and went back to the living-room. Though the Bracketts were ten years older than he and Jen-nifer were, they seemed ten years younger than he and his wife had ever been. He hated to see them move away.

When he heard Jennifer bring the car back, he walked into the kitchen and passed on the Bracketts' invitation.

"I don't feel up to your friends tonight," she snapped. "I'm going up to my bed."

The way she emphasized "my bed" showed him how much things had changed since he'd left home for the shopping plaza a short time before. He watched her slim legs cross the kitchen and disappear up the back stairs.

"The happiest man in the world," he said, now mocking the way he'd said it earlier in the evening. Then he laughed a bitter, joyless laugh. Taking one of the bottles of Scotch from the bag on the table, and without following his usual routine of shutting the garage door or putting out the lights, he went through the house to the front door, opened it, and slammed it noisily behind him. With the bottle swinging in his hand he headed across the street to where the beckoning lights, and life and love, shone through the Bracketts' picture window.

THEY EAT OUT
Margaret Atwood

In restaurants we argue
over which of us will pay for your funeral

though the real question is
whether or not I will make you immortal.

At the moment only I
can do it and so

I raise the magic fork
over the plate of beef fried rice

and plunge it into your heart.
There is a faint pop, a sizzle

and through your own split head
you rise up glowing;

the ceiling opens
a voice sings Love Is A Many

Splendoured Thing
you hang suspended above the city

in blue tights and a red cape,
your eyes flashing in unison.

The other diners regard you
some with awe, some only with boredom:

they cannot decide if you are a new weapon
or only a new advertisement.

As for me, I continue eating;
I liked you better the way you were,
but you were always ambitious.

THE STENOGRAPHERS
P.K. Page

After the brief bivouac of Sunday,
their eyes, in the forced march of Monday to Saturday,
hoist the white flag, flutter in the snow-storm of paper,
haul it down and crack in the mid-sun of temper.

In the pause between the first draft and the carbon
they glimpse the smooth hours when they were children —
the ride in the ice-cart, the ice-man's name,
the end of the route and the long walk home;

remember the sea where floats at high tide
were sea marrows growing on the scatter-green vine
or spools of grey toffee, or wasps' nests on water;
remember the sand and the leaves of the country.

Bell rings and they go and the voice draws their pencil
like a sled across snow; when its runners are frozen
rope snaps and the voice then is pulling no burden
but runs like a dog on the winter of paper.

Their climates are winter and summer — no wind
for the kites of their hearts — no wind for a flight;
a breeze at the most, to tumble them over
and leave them like rubbish — the boy-friends of blood.

In the inch of the noon as they move they are stagnant.
The terrible calm of the noon is their anguish;
the lip of the counter, the shapes of the straws
like icicles breaking their tongues, are invaders.

Their beds are their oceans — salt water of weeping
the waves that they know — the tide before sleep;
and fighting to drown they assemble their sheep
in columns and watch them leap desks for their fences
and stare at them with their own mirror-worn faces.

In the felt of the morning the calico-minded,
sufficiently starched, insert papers, hit keys,
efficient and sure as their adding machines;
yet they weep in the vault, they are taut as net curtains
stretched upon frames. In their eyes I have seen
the pin men of madness in marathon trim
race round the track of the stadium pupil.

FLYING A RED KITE
Hugh Hood

The ride home began badly. Still almost a stranger to the city,
tired, hot and dirty, and inattentive to his surroundings, Fred
stood for ten minutes, shifting his parcels from arm to arm
and his weight from one leg to the other, in a sweaty bath of
shimmering glare from the sidewalk, next to a grimy yellow-
and-black bus stop. To his left a line of murmuring would-be
passengers lengthened until there were enough to fill any vehi-
cle that might come for them. Finally an obese brown bus
waddled up like an indecent old cow and stopped with an ex-
piring moo at the head of the line. Fred was glad to be first in
line, as there didn't seem to be room for more than a few to
embus.

But as he stepped up he noticed a sign in the window
which said *Côte des Neiges — Boulevard* and he recoiled as
though bitten, trampling the toes of the woman behind him
and making her squeal. It was a Sixty-six bus, not the Sixty-
five that he wanted. The woman pushed furiously past him
while the remainder of the line clamoured in the rear. He
stared at the number on the bus stop: Sixty-six, not his stop at
all. Out of the corner of his eye he saw another coach pulling
away from the stop on the northeast corner, the right stop, the
Sixty-five, and the one he should have been standing under all
this time. Giving his characteristic weary put-upon sigh,
which he used before breakfast to annoy Naomi, he adjusted
his parcels in both arms, feeling sweat run around his neck
and down his collar between his shoulders, and crossed Saint
Catherine against the light, drawing a Gallic sneer from a
policeman, to stand for several more minutes at the head of a
new queue, under the right sign. It was nearly four-thirty and
the Saturday shopping crowds wanted to get home, out of the
summer dust and heat, out of the jitter of the big July holiday
weekend. They would all go home and sit on their balconies.
All over the suburbs in duplexes and fourplexes, families
would be enjoying cold suppers in the open air on their balconies; but the Calverts' apartment had none. Fred and Naomi
had been ignorant of the meaning of the custom when they

were apartment hunting. They had thought of Montreal as a city of the Sub-Arctic and in the summers they would have leisure to repent the misjudgment.

He had been shopping along the length of Saint Catherine between Peel and Guy, feeling guilty because he had heard for years that this was where all those pretty Montreal women made their promenade; he had wanted to watch without familial encumbrances. There had been girls enough but nothing outrageously special, so he had beguiled the scorching afternoon making a great many small idle purchases, of the kind one does when trapped in a Woolworth's. A ball-point pen and a note-pad for Naomi, who was always stealing his and leaving it in the kitchen with long, wildly optimistic grocery lists scribbled in it. Six packages of cigarettes, some legal-size envelopes, two Dinky-toys, a long-playing record, two parcels of second-hand books, and the lightest of his burdens and the unhandiest, the kite he had bought for Deedee, two flimsy wooden sticks rolled up in red plastic film, and a ball of cheap thin string — not enough, by the look of it, if he should ever get the thing into the air.

When he'd gone fishing, as a boy, he'd never caught any fish; when playing hockey he had never been able to put the puck in the net. One by one the wholesome outdoor sports and games had defeated him. But he had gone on believing in them, in their curative moral values, and now he hoped that Deedee, though a girl, might sometime catch a fish; and though she obviously wouldn't play hockey, she might ski, or toboggan on the mountain. He had noticed that people treated kites and kite-flying as somehow holy. They were a natural symbol, thought Fred, and he felt uneasily sure that he would have trouble getting this one to fly.

The inside of the bus was shaped like a box-car with windows, but the windows were useless. You might have peeled off the bus as you'd peel the paper off a pound of butter, leaving an oblong yellow lump of thick solid heat, with the passengers embedded in it like hopeless bread-crumbs.

He elbowed and wriggled his way along the aisle, feeling a

momentary shiver of pleasure as his palm rubbed accidentally along the back of a girl's skirt — once, a philosopher — the sort of thing you couldn't be charged with. But you couldn't get away with it twice and anyway the girl either didn't feel it, or had no idea who had caressed her. There were vacant seats towards the rear, which was odd because the bus was otherwise full, and he struggled towards them, trying not to break the wooden struts which might be persuaded to fly. The bus lurched forward and his feet moved with the floor, causing him to pop suddenly out of the crowd by the exit, into a square well of space next to the heat and stink of the engine. He swayed around and aimed himself at a narrow vacant seat, nearly dropping a parcel of books as he lowered himself precipitately into it.

The bus crossed Sherbrooke Street and began, intolerably slowly, to crawl up Côte des Neiges and around the western spur of the mountain. His ears began to pick up the usual mélange of French and English and to sort it out; he was proud of his French and pleased that most of the people on the streets spoke a less correct, though more fluent, version than his own. He had found that he could make his customers understand him perfectly — he was a book salesman — but that people on the street were happier when he addressed them in English.

The chatter in the bus grew clearer and more interesting and he began to listen, grasping all at once why he had found a seat back here. He was sitting next to a couple of drunks who emitted an almost overpowering smell of beer. They were cheerfully exchanging indecencies and obscure jokes and in a minute they would speak to him. They always did, drunks and panhandlers, finding some soft fearfulness in his face which exposed him as a shrinking easy mark. Once in a railroad station he had been approached three times in twenty minutes by the same panhandler on his rounds. Each time he had given the man something, despising himself with each new weakness.

The cheerful pair sitting at right-angles to him grew louder and more blunt and the women within earshot grew glum. There was no harm in it; there never is. But you avoid your neighbour's eye, afraid of smiling awkwardly, or of looking offended and a prude.

"Now this Pearson," said one of the revellers, "he's just a little short-ass. He's just a little fellow without any brains. Why, some of the speeches he makes . . . I could make them myself. I'm an old Tory myself, an old Tory."

"I'm an old Blue," said the other.

"Is that so, now? That's fine, a fine thing." Fred was sure he didn't know what a Blue was.

"I'm a Balliol man. Whoops!" They began to make monkey-like noises to annoy the passengers and amuse themselves. "Whoops," said the Oxford man again, "hoo, hoo, there's one now, there's one for you." He was talking about a girl on the sidewalk.

"She's a one, now, isn't she? Look at the legs on her, oh, look at them now, isn't that something?" There was a noisy clearing of throats and the same voice said something that sounded like "Shaoil-na-baig".

"Oh, good, good!" said the Balliol man.

"Shaoil-na-baig," said the other loudly, "I've not forgotten my Gaelic, do you see, shaoil-na-baig," he said it loudly, and a woman up the aisle reddened and looked away. It sounded like a dirty phrase to Fred, delivered as though the speaker had forgotten all his Gaelic but the words for sexual intercourse.

"And how is your French, Father?" asked the Balliol man, and the title made Fred start in his seat. He pretended to drop a parcel and craned his head quickly sideways. The older of the two drunks, the one sitting by the window, examining the passing legs and skirts with the same impulse that Fred had felt on Saint Catherine Street, was indeed a priest, and couldn't possibly be an impostor. His clerical suit was too well-worn, egg-stained and blemished with candle-droppings, and fit its wearer too well, for it to be an assumed costume.

The face was unmistakably a southern Irishman's. The priest darted a quick peek into Fred's eyes before he could turn them away, giving a monkey-like grimace that might have been a mixture of embarrassment and shame but probably wasn't.

He was a little gray-haired bucko of close to sixty, with a triangular, sly, mottled crimson face and uneven yellow teeth. His hands moved jerkily and expressively in his lap, in counterpoint to the lively intelligent movements of his face.

The other chap, the Balliol man, was a perfect type of English-speaking Montrealer, perhaps a bond salesman or minor functionary in a brokerage house on Saint James Street. He was about fifty with a round-domed head, red hair beginning to go slightly white at the neck and ears, pink porcine skin, very neatly barbered and combed. He wore an expensive white shirt with a fine blue stripe and there was some sort of ring around his tie. He had his hands folded fatly on the knob of a stick, round face with deep laugh-lines in the cheeks, and a pair of cheerfully darting little blue-bloodshot eyes. Where could the pair have run into each other?

"I've forgotten my French years ago," said the priest carelessly. "I was down in New Brunswick for many years and I'd no use for it, the work I was doing. I'm Irish, you know."

"I'm an old Blue."

"That's right," said the priest, "John's the boy. Oh, he's a sharp lad is John. He'll let them all get off, do you see, to Manitoba for the summer, and bang, BANG!" All the bus jumped. "He'll call an election on them and then they'll run." Something caught his eye and he turned to gaze out the window. The bus was moving slowly past the cemetery of Notre Dame des Neiges and the priest stared, half-sober, at the graves stretched up the mountainside in the sun.

"I'm not in there," he said involuntarily.

"Indeed you're not," said his companion, "lots of life in you yet, eh, Father?"

"Oh," he said, "oh, I don't think I'd know what to do with a girl if I fell over one." He looked out at the cemetery for several moments. "It's all a sham," he said, half under his breath, "they're in there for good." He swung around and looked innocently at Fred. "Are you going fishing, lad?"

"It's a kite that I bought for my little girl," said Fred, more cheerfully than he felt.

"She'll enjoy that, she will," said the priest, "for it's grand sport."

"Go fly a kite!" said the Oxford man hilariously. It amused him and he said it again. "Go fly a kite!" He and the priest began to chant together, "Hoo, hoo, whoops," and they laughed and in a moment, clearly, would begin to sing.

The bus turned lumberingly onto Queen Mary Road. Fred stood up confusedly and began to push his way towards the rear door. As he turned away, the priest grinned impudently at him, stammering a jolly goodbye. Fred was too embarrassed to answer but he smiled uncertainly and fled. He heard them take up their chant anew.

"Hoo, there's a one for you, hoo. Shaoil-na-baig. Whoops!" Their laughter died out as the bus rolled heavily away.

He had heard about such men, naturally, and knew that they existed; but it was the first time in Fred's life that he had ever seen a priest misbehave himself publicly. There are so many priests in the city, he thought, that the number of bum ones must be in proportion. The explanation satisfied him but the incident left a disagreeable impression in his mind.

Safely home he took his shirt off and poured himself a Coke. Then he allowed Deedee, who was dancing around him with her terrible energy, to open the parcels.

"Give your Mummy the pad and pencil, sweetie," he directed. She crossed obediently to Naomi's chair and handed her the cheap plastic case.

"Let me see you make a note in it," he said, "make a list of something, for God's sake, so you'll remember it's yours. And the one on the desk is mine. Got that?" He spoke without rancour or much interest; it was a rather overworked joke between them.

"What's this?" said Deedee, holding up the kite and allowing the ball of string to roll down the hall. He resisted a compulsive wish to get up and re-wind the string.

"It's for you. Don't you know what it is?"

"It's a red kite," she said. She had wanted one for weeks but spoke now as if she weren't interested. Then all at once she grew very excited and eager. "Can you put it together right now?" she begged.

"I think we'll wait till after supper, sweetheart," he said, feeling mean. You raised their hopes and then dashed them; there was no real reason why they shouldn't put it together now, except his fatigue. He looked pleadingly at Naomi.

"Daddy's tired, Deedee," she said obligingly, "he's had a long hot afternoon."

"But I want to see it," said Deedee, fiddling with the flimsy red film and nearly puncturing it.

Fred was sorry he'd drunk a Coke; it bloated him and upset his stomach and had no true cooling effect.

"We'll have something to eat," he said cajolingly, "and then Mummy can put it together for you." He turned to his wife. "You don't mind, do you? I'd only spoil the thing." Threading a needle or hanging a picture made the normal slight tremor of his hands accentuate itself almost embarrassingly.

"Of course not," she said, smiling wryly. They had long ago worked out their areas of uselessness.

"There's a picture on it, and directions."

"Yes. Well, we'll get it together somehow. Flying it . . . that's something else again." She got up, holding the note-pad, and went into the kitchen to put the supper on.

It was a good hot-weather supper, tossed greens with the correct proportions of vinegar and oil, croissants and butter, and cold sliced ham. As he ate, his spirits began to percolate a bit, and he gave Naomi a graphic sketch of the incident on the bus. "It depressed me," he told her. This came as no surprise to her; almost anything unusual, which he couldn't do anything to alter or relieve, depressed Fred nowadays. "He must have been sixty. Oh, quite sixty, I should think, and you could tell that everything had come to pieces for him."

"It's a standard story," she said, "and aren't you sentimentalizing it?"

"In what way?"

"The 'spoiled priest' business, the empty man, the man without a calling. They all write about that. Graham Greene made his whole career out of that."

"That isn't what the phrase means," said Fred laboriously. "It doesn't refer to a man who actually *is* a priest, though without a vocation."

"No?" She lifted an eyebrow; she was better educated than he.

"No, it doesn't. It means somebody who never became a priest at all. The point is that you *had* a vocation but ignored it. That's what a spoiled priest is. It's an Irish phrase, and usually refers to somebody who is a failure and who drinks too much." He laughed shortly. "I don't qualify, on the second count."

"You're not a failure."

"No, I'm too young. Give me time!" There was no reason for him to talk like this; he was a very productive salesman.

"You certainly never wanted to be a priest," she said positively, looking down at her breasts and laughing, thinking of some secret. "I'll bet you never considered it, not with your habits." She meant his bedroom habits, which were ardent, and in which she ardently acquiesced. She was an adept and enthusiastic partner, her greatest gift as a wife.

"Let's put that kite together," said Deedee, getting up from her little table, with such adult decision that her parents chuckled. "Come on," she said, going to the sofa and bouncing up and down.

30

Naomi put a tear in the fabric right away, on account of the ambiguity of the directions. There should have been two holes in the kite, through which a lugging-string passed; but the holes hadn't been provided and when she put them there with the point of an icepick they immediately began to grow.

"Scotch tape," she said, like a surgeon asking for sutures.

"There's a picture on the front," said Fred, secretly cross but ostensibly helpful.

"I see it," she said.

"Mummy put holes in the kite," said Deedee with alarm. "Is she going to break it?"

"No," said Fred. The directions were certainly ambiguous.

Naomi tied the struts at right-angles, using so much string that Fred was sure the kite would be too heavy. Then she strung the fabric on the notched ends of the struts and the thing began to take shape.

"It doesn't look quite right," she said, puzzled and irritated.

"The surface has to be curved so there's a difference of air pressure." He remembered this, rather unfairly, from high-school physics classes.

She bent the cross-piece and tied it in a bowed arc, and the red film pulled taut. "There now," she said.

"You've forgotten the lugging-string on the front," said Fred critically, "that's what you made the holes for, remember?"

"Why is Daddy mad?" said Deedee.

"i'm not mad!"

It had begun to shower, great pear-shaped drops of rain falling with a plop on the sidewalk.

"That's as close as I can come," said Naomi, staring at Fred, "we aren't going to try it tonight, are we?"

"We promised her," he said, "and it's only a light rain."

"Will we all go?"

"I wish you'd take her," he said, "because my stomach feels upset. I should never drink Coca-Cola."

31

"It always bothers you..You should know that by now."

"I'm not running out on you," he said anxiously, "and if you can't make it work, I'll take her up tomorrow afternoon."

"I know," she said, "come on, Deedee, we're going to take the kite up the hill." They left the house and crossed the street. Fred watched them through the window as they started up the steep path hand in hand. He felt left out, and slightly nauseated.

They were back in half an hour, their spirits not at all dampened, which surprised him.

"No go, eh?"

"Much too wet, and not enough breeze. The rain knocks it flat."

"O.K.!" he exclaimed with fervour. "I'll try tomorrow."

"We'll try again tomorrow," said Deedee with equal determination — her parents mustn't forget their obligations.

Sunday afternoon the weather was nearly perfect, hot, clear, a firm steady breeze but not too much of it, and a cloudless sky. At two o'clock Fred took his daughter by the hand and they started up the mountain together, taking the path through the woods that led up to the University parking lots.

"We won't come down until we make it fly," Fred swore, "that's a promise."

"Good," she said, hanging on to his hand and letting him drag her up the steep path, "there are lots of bugs in here, aren't there?"

"Yes," he said briefly — he was being liberally bitten.

When they came to the end of the path, they saw that the campus was deserted and still, and there was all kinds of running room. Fred gave Deedee careful instructions about where to sit, and what to do if a car should come along, and then he paid out a little string and began to run across the parking lot towards the main building of the University. He felt a tug at the string and throwing a glance over his shoulder he saw the kite bobbing in the air, about twenty feet off the ground. He let out more string, trying to keep it filled with air, but he couldn't run quite fast enough, and in a moment it fell back to the ground.

"Nearly had it!" he shouted to Deedee, whom he'd left fifty yards behind.

"Daddy, Daddy, come back," she hollered apprehensively. Rolling up the string as he went, he retraced his steps and prepared to try again. It was important to catch a gust of wind and run into it. On the second try the kite went higher than before but as he ran past the entrance to the University he felt the air pressure lapse and saw the kite waver and fall. He walked slowly back, realizing that the bulk of the main building was cutting off the air currents.

"We'll go up higher," he told her, and she seized his hand and climbed obediently up the road beside him, around behind the main building, past ash barrels and trash heaps; they climbed a flight of wooden steps, crossed a parking lot next to L'Ecole Polytechnique and a slanting field further up, and at last came to a pebbly dirt road that ran along the top ridge of the mountain beside the cemetery. Fred remembered the priest as he looked across the fence and along the broad stretch of cemetery land rolling away down the slope of the mountain to the west. They were about six hundred feet above the river, he judged. He'd never been up this far before.

"My sturdy little brown legs are tired," Deedee remarked, and he burst out laughing.

"Where did you hear that," he said, "who has sturdy little brown legs?"

She screwed her face up in a grin. "The gingerbread man," she said, beginning to sing, "I can run away from you, I can, 'cause I'm the little gingerbread man."

The air was dry and clear and without a trace of humidity and the sunshine was dazzling. On either side of the dirt road grew great clumps of wild flowers, yellow and blue, buttercups, daisies and goldenrod, and cornflowers and clover. Deedee disappeared into the flowers — picking bouquets was her favourite game. He could see the shrubs and grasses heave and sway as she moved around. The scent of clover and of dry sweet grass was very keen here, and from the east, over the curved top of the mountain, the wind blew in a steady un-eddying stream. Five or six miles off to the southwest he spied the wide intensely gray-white stripe of the river. He heard Deedee cry: "Daddy, Daddy, come and look." He pushed through the coarse grasses and found her.

"Berries," she cried rapturously, "look at all the berries! Can I eat them?" She had found a wild raspberry bush, a thing he hadn't seen since he was six years old. He'd never expected to find one growing in the middle of Montreal.

"Wild raspberries," he said wonderingly, "sure you can pick them dear; but be careful of the prickles." They were all shades and degrees of ripeness from black to vermilion.

"Ouch," said Deedee, pricking her fingers as she pulled off the berries. She put a handful in her mouth and looked wry.

"Are they bitter?"

"Juicy," she mumbled with her mouth full. A trickle of dark juice ran down her chin.

"Eat some more," he said, "while I try the kite again." She bent absorbedly to the task of hunting them out, and he walked down the road for some distance and then turned to run up towards her. This time he gave the kite plenty of string before he began to move; he ran as hard as he could, panting and handing the string out over his shoulders, burning his fingers as it slid through them. All at once he felt the line pull and pulse as if there were a living thing on the other end and he turned on his heel and watched while the kite danced into the upper air-currents above the treetops and began to soar up and up. He gave it more line and in an instant it pulled high up away from him across the fence, two hundred feet and more above him up over the cemetery where it steadied and hung, bright red in the sunshine. He thought flashingly of the priest saying, "It's all a sham," and he knew all at once that the priest was wrong. Deedee came running down to him, laughing with excitement and pleasure and singing joyfully about the gingerbread man, and he knelt in the dusty roadway and put his arms around her, placing her hands on the line between his. They gazed, squinting in the sun, at the flying red thing, and he turned away and saw in the shadow of her cheek and on her lips and chin the dark rich red of the pulp and juice of the crushed raspberries.

WARREN PRYOR
Alden Nowlan

When every pencil meant a sacrifice
his parents boarded him at school in town,
slaving to free him from the stony fields,
the meagre acreage that bore them down.

They blushed with pride when, at his graduation,
they watched him picking up the slender scroll,
his passport from the years of brutal toil
and lonely patience in a barren hole.

When he went in the Bank their cups ran over.
They marvelled how he wore a milk-white shirt
work days and jeans on Sundays. He was saved
from their thistle-strewn farm and its red dirt.

And he said nothing. Hard and serious
like a young bear inside his teller's cage,
his axe-hewn hands upon the paper bills
aching with empty strength and throttled rage.

ON SAINT-URBAIN STREET
Milton Acorn

My room's bigger than a coffin
but not so well made.
The couple on my left drink, and
at two a.m. the old man shouts
of going back to Russia.
About five he or his wrung-out wife
puke up their passage money.

The janitor (pay, five a week
plus a one-bed apartment
with furnace in kitchen) has
one laughing babe at home
and two girls, for lack of room,

in the orphanage.
On holidays they appear
with their soul-smashed faces.

Upstairs the Negro girl
answers the phone, sings my name
in a voice like a bad angel's.
Her boyfriends change
every weekend, like the movies.
But my room's cheap, tho'
when the wind shifts north
I wear my overcoat
to type this bitter little poem.

WOMEN IN ADVERTISING
Katherine McGillivray

I'm fed up to my head and shoulders with advertising that insults women. And I'm also puzzled, to the tips of my Revlon-painted toenails, by an advertising approach that holds 51% of its customers in utter contempt. We are shown as kitchen lackeys — and while the woman does the menial work, there's a man doing the voice over. Man sells, woman slaves.

The time has come for advertising men to liberate themselves from their false idea of women. Don't they realize how many working-age women are out working today? Half the women in the country are simply not at home when The Fag with A Bag — I mean, the Man from Glad — drops in. They're at their desks, their factory benches, or their seats in the Boardroom.

Now, I really don't think that all advertisers are male chauvinist pigs, but I do think that they're missing out on their market. Contempt for their female 51% of the buying public leads them into some very curious advertising. Do they really think we believe in fairies? Like that awful Man from Glad? Do they think we sit at home, hoping Mr. Clean and those other weirdos will drop by?

When they go home to their wives and girlfriends, do they ask them: "Seen the White Knight today, honey?" Do they look out of their picture windows and shout: "Hey! It's a white tornado!" If not, why not? If they don't talk to their own women that way, why do they do so to the rest of us?

Why have they created this extraordinary image of us? How long will it be before they liberate us women from this hopelessly distorted picture they present of us? It had better be soon. For I believe that this liberation is a great deal more important than they seem to imagine.

What kind of homes are advertisers forcing upon us? With floors that mustn't be stepped on, kitchens where nobody cooks, with an atmosphere like a hospital ward.

Correction. Somebody is allowed to cook — but only grandma. And only cake-mix. You see the old bag leering over her steel-rimmed glasses. Mother doesn't cook. She serves. She serves Instant Breakfast to a bunch of layabouts who can't crawl out of bed ten minutes earlier to get to the office or school on time. She beams with motherly pride as her children stuff their faces with food. She's forever shoving food down people. Usually cheap food, closely followed by expensive aspirins and remedies for acid indigestion. Which is probably why one seldom sees her eating.

Even when there's a party, she's there with her tray. Fetching and carrying like crazy. Then her husband turns round and shouts at her because she's bought bitter coffee. Or the Ajax has turned blue. Or she's starched his socks. And her daughter whines: "Wouldn't you know — my big chance! A date with George, and I'm all out of mouthwash!" What a crew. My grandmother the cake-mix cook. My husband Attila the Hun. My son the gobbler. My daughter the gargler. Family life of a wife and mother, courtesy of the advertising industry.

Thanks a whole lot. We haven't come as far as you might think, baby. We've still a helluva way to go.

Have they ever stopped to think of the overall picture this approach presents of Canadian womanhood? A sort of white female Stepin Fetchit, a lackey chained to her kitchen, with underarms like the Sahara, her scalp as flakeless as a billiard ball, breathing hexachlorophene over the Man from Glad, comparing the whiteness of washes from dawn till dusk with some seedy idiot with a microphone, doling out cardboard cornflakes and great dollops of monosodium glutamate and carrying plates, carrying trays, carrying, carrying. Not much of a picture, is it? No wonder so many daughters, alarmed at the prospect of living like this, are taking off to communes.

So far, I've done nothing but complain about the image advertising men have created of women. But now I'm going to unburden myself of some advice which, if followed — and I have no reason to doubt that it will be — will liberate us women from where we sit. At the bottom of our broken pedestals.

Here's what advertisers can do for us. Show us as intelligent human beings, not as if we had all had prefrontal lobotomies.

Stop portraying us as ill-mannered witches who sneer at the whiteness (or non-whiteness) of each other's laundry and sniff for cabbage smells. Show us with a reasonable standard of human behavior and decent feelings.

Stop talking down to women. Talk *to* us.

THE REALM OF CHILDHOOD
Pierre Vallières

While my father was expanding the house, to make it more liveable, my mother hardly dared invite "the relatives" to visit us. She was so ashamed of "the surroundings", as she said. In spite of the misery that encircled and penetrated his domain, my father was happy to have something to build ... even if it was only an extension to this jerry-built shack. But my mother dreaded letting others — city people — see our poverty.

It was as if our entire existence was nothing but a daily obscenity. We had to hide *that* from the people of the big city.

But the people of the big city and the rest of the province soon learned the truth ... from the newspaper headlines in capital letters reading: "THE WHOLE TRUTH ABOUT VILLE JACQUES-CARTIER" — "BABIES DYING OF COLD IN COTEAU-ROUGE" — "TERRIBLE POVERTY ACROSS THE BRIDGE" — "A CITY OF SHEET-METAL" — etc. We would read these reports with rage in our hearts. What were we *guilty* of? Of having wanted freedom? We had never had it. Painfully, we were trying to achieve it. Why did these newspapers talk about us as if we were barbarians spewed out by Montreal, like bile spewed out by an unhealthy liver?

For some newspapers, which I need not name, we were not men but "the dirty masses" of Ville Jacques-Cartier, the human "scrap" of the biggest garbage dump in the metropolitan area.

After the stories in the newspapers came the "collections", the distributions of food and whatnot, the *charity* of all the people who had guilty consciences or who simply adored helping the poor. Fortunately, we were not armed; otherwise the Church would have acquired a few more martyrs and the statue manufacturers would have made money.

Everything was increasing: the population, the slums, the publicity, the taxes, the number of unemployed, of sick or crippled children, and of unwed mothers, the churches, the thugs, the grocers, the thieves, the murderers, the drunks, the wretched ...

Angus Shops, Vickers, Canada Cement, Canadair, etc., were laying off hundreds of workers every week. And each time the unions said it would only be temporary.

Some families converted their sheds into lodgings, moved into them, and rented out their shacks . . . so as to be able to buy enough "baloney" and Weston bread to feed the "little ones". Others sold their houses — because of the taxes — and went off to build others in Saint-Amable or Sainte-Julie, beyond Boucherville.

More than one mother tore her hair in despair, and more than one man thought of stealing, killing, or committing suicide. Some set fire to their houses in order to collect the insurance and try to start over again somewhere else. The Established Order declared that henceforth laziness and slovenliness would be forbidden in Ville Jacques-Cartier, that norms would be established, that those who did not meet them would be expelled, and that taxes would be raised in order to force the "lazy" (that is, the unemployed) to leave the city. The underworld, which with the support of Duplessis controlled the city, tried to put up a respectable front and held numerous press conferences announcing reforms such as Quebec had never known. They began to build schools and distribute little gifts to their friends. Overnight, grocers, wrestlers, bandits became "entrepreneurs" and contractors for primary schools, churches, and administrative buildings. All this was financed with government subsidies or "Sunday collections" — in other words, with money stolen from the people, with the broad, hypocritical smile of a gentleman-thief. The purpose of building schools was not to educate children, but to grant "paying" contracts to supporters of the regime. So it was that Duplessis, financed by his friends on Wall Street, created his own class of petty bourgeois out of the very misery of the workers and farmers of Quebec who, taken in by a cunningly organized system of patronage, voted for him *en masse* — *against* their true interests and without quite realizing what was going on.

42

Around 1950, a vast, slow construction project was undertaken to provide a complete system of aqueducts and sewers for the "dirty masses" of Ville Jacques-Cartier. The underworld rubbed its hands at the thought of the enormous profits it would reap from this very humanitarian enterprise. They began by raising taxes. One after another, all the streets of the city were transformed into long trenches eight feet deep, with heaps of earth on either side about six feet high. Paths were improvised between the houses, piles of earth, trenches, sewer pipes, dynamite, steam shovels, etc. The daily dynamiting cracked the walls of the shacks and ruined the wells, which ran dry or filled with muddy water. A few public drinking fountains were installed here and there, on the privileged streets, which were served by the aqueduct from the first year on. But after a lightning beginning, the work slowed down. Everywhere there were trenches, unusable wells, and mud . . . mountains of mud. And the work did not progress: lack of funds, people said. But Quebec had put millions into the project. Where had the money gone? The people asked questions while the months and years passed. The work advanced at a snail's pace, a little here, a little there. In winter all the machines fell silent. The long trenches filled up with snow.

Most families had to collect rain water in huge barrels or buy water by the pail every day from a tradesman to whom the city authorities had granted a monopoly on the sale of water. Water cost five cents a pail. Many families, including mine, had to tighten their belts to buy water for cooking, bathing, doing laundry, etc.

That lasted for years, years during which Duplessis was letting the Americans loot the rich iron deposits of northern Quebec.

The Americans were making billions off *our* iron, Duplessis was making millions off the Americans, the political machine of the National Union Party was distributing its millions to the supporters and thugs of the regime . . . and we, poor starving wretches, we had to buy water!

As this situation went on and on, people tried to find ways of getting free water. Some of them walked a mile or two every day to fill a few pails at the fountain on one or another of the privileged streets, the streets that *had* water. But that was not always possible, either because the weather was bad or because the trips were too tiring.

My family lived about two thousand feet from the new Longueuil, where modern cottages were being built for the petty-bourgeois families who wanted to live in the suburbs. Together with our neighbors, we tried to get *permission* from these richer suburbanites to take the water we needed from the fountains in their quarter, whose streets were already paved with asphalt. They treated us with unbelievable contempt (and yet they were not English). A few weeks after they had spat in our faces, the petty bourgeois of new Longueuil built a high wooden fence so they would not have to meet the thirsty eyes of the "dirty people" every day. All the streets which up until then had crossed Longueuil, new Longueuil, and Ville Jacques-Cartier were blocked off at the border of Ville Jacques-Cartier and new Longueuil. (With the exception, however, of Saint-Alexandre Street and the Chambly road.)

If a revolutionary party had existed in Quebec at that time, it would have found thousands of workers, women, and young people ready to take up arms in Ville Jacques-Cartier. Some people thought about that possibility, but without acting on it. There were many street fights with picks and shovels, but nothing lasting. Only, the consumption of beer rose steadily.

Senseless crimes were reported daily. My mother dreamed of leaving this accursed city. But where was the money to come from? In this atmosphere of desolation, increased by the vast, unfinished construction works and the water shortage, to try to sell the shack would have been to fly in the face of common sense. *We waited,* we survived everything, like thousands of other men, women, and children who did not have the means to escape from their absurd condition. We waited for it to be over . . . the way, in 1940, people had waited for the war to be over so they could learn how to live once more.

Weariness, bitterness, and resignation again followed upon disappointed hopes and took possession of the manipulated, despised, worn out, powerless, demoralized people.

THE GREENWOOD SHADE
Alexander McLachlan

Oh, seek the greenwood shade,
   Away from the city din,
From heartless strife of trade,
   From fumes of beer and gin;
Where Commerce spreads her fleets,
   Where bloated Luxury lies,
Where lean Want prowls the streets,
   And stares with wolfish eyes.

Flee from the city's sin,
   Its many-color'd code,
Its palaces raised to sin,
   Its temples rear'd to God;
Its cellars dark and dank,
   Where ne'er a sunbeam falls,
'Mid faces lean and lank
   As the hungry-looking walls;

Its fest'ring pits of woe,
   Its teeming earthly hells,
Whose surges ever flow
   In sound of Sabbath bells.
O God! I'd rather be
   An Indian in the wood,
To range through forest free
   In search of daily food.

Oh! rather I'd pursue
   The wolf and grizzly bear,
Than toil for the thankless few
   In seething pits of care.
Here Winter's breath is rude,
   His fingers cold and wan;
But what's his wildest mood
   To the tyranny of man?

To trackless forest wild,
    To loneliest abode,
The heart is reconciled
    That's felt Oppression's load.
The desert place is bright,
    The wilderness is fair,
If Hope but shed her light —
    If Freedom be but there.

TREE IN A STREET
Louis Dudek

Why will not that tree adapt itself to our tempo?
We have lopped off several branches,
cut her skin to the white bone,
run wires through her body and her loins,
yet she will not change.
Ignorant of traffic, of dynamos and steel,
as uncontemporary
as bloomers and bustles
she stands there like a green cliché.

THE BIRTH OF GOD
Lionel Kearns

```
        11111111111
     1111111111111111111
    111111111111111111111
   11111111111111111111111
11111                 11111
11111         000     11111
11111      000000     11111
11111   000000000     11111
11111   000000000     11111
11111     0000000     11111
11111     0000000     11111
11111     0000000     11111
11111     0000000     11111
11111     0000000     11111
11111     0000000     11111
11111     0000000     11111
11111     0000000     11111
11111     0000000     11111
11111     0000000     11111
11111     0000000     11111
11111   00000000000   11111
11111   00000000000   11111
11111                 11111
  1111111111111111111111111
   11111111111111111111
    11111111111111111
      11111111111
```

THE CITY OF THE END OF THINGS
Archibald Lampman

Beside the pounding cataracts
Of midnight streams unknown to us
'Tis builded in the leafless tracts
And valleys huge of Tartarus.
Lurid and lofty and vast it seems;
It hath no rounded name that rings,
But I have heard it called in dreams
The City of the End of Things.

Its roofs and iron towers have grown
None knoweth how high within the night,
But in its murky streets far down
A flaming terrible and bright
Shakes all the stalking shadows there,
Across the walls, across the floors,
And shifts upon the upper air
From out a thousand furnace doors;
And all the while an awful sound
Keeps roaring on continually,
And crashes in the ceaseless round
Of a gigantic harmony.
Through its grim depths re-echoing
And all its weary height of walls,
With measured roar and iron ring,
The inhuman music lifts and falls.
Where no thing rests and no man is,
And only fire and night hold sway;
The beat, the thunder and the hiss
Cease not, and change not, night nor day.
And moving at unheard commands,
The abysses and vast fires between,
Flit figures that with clanking hands
Obey a hideous routine;
They are not flesh, they are not bone,
They see not with the human eye,

And from their iron lips is blown
A dreadful and monotonous cry;
And whoso of our mortal race
Should find that city unaware,
Lean Death would smite him face to face,
And blanch him with its venomed air:
Or caught by the terrific spell,
Each thread of memory snapt and cut,
His soul would shrivel and its shell
Go rattling like an empty nut.

It was not always so, but once,
In days that no man thinks upon,
Fair voices echoed from its stones,
The light above it leaped and shone:
Once there were multitudes of men,
That built that city in their pride,
Until its might was made, and then
They withered age by age and died.
But now of that prodigious race,
Three only in an iron tower,
Set like carved idols face to face,
Remain the masters of its power;
And at the city gate a fourth,
Gigantic and with dreadful eyes,
Sits looking toward the lightless north,
Beyond the reach of memories;
Fast rooted to the lurid floor,
A bulk that never moves a jot,
In his pale body dwells no more,
Or mind or soul, — an idiot!
But sometime in the end those three
Shall perish and their hands be still,
And with the master's touch shall flee
Their incommunicable skill.

A stillness absolute as death
Along the slacking wheels shall lie,
And, flagging at a single breath,
The fires shall moulder out and die.
The roar shall vanish at its height,
And over that tremendous town
The silence of eternal night
Shall gather close and settle down.
All its grim grandeur, tower and hall,
Shall be abandoned utterly,
And into rust and dust shall fall
From century to century;
Nor ever living thing shall grow,
Nor trunk of tree, nor blade of grass;
No drop shall fall, no wind shall blow,
Nor sound of any foot shall pass:
Alone of its accursèd state,
One thing the hand of Time shall spare,
For the grim Idiot at the gate
Is deathless and eternal there.

SALE NIGHT IN WINKLER
Heather Robertson

Honk if you Love Jesus!
(Bumper sticker, Winkler, Manitoba)

It's a bad night for a sale, but the flyers have been out for days now, stuffed into 20,000 mailboxes in Winkler, Morden, Horndean, Rosenfeld, St. Jean, Gretna, Altona, Manitou, and Plum Coulee. In fact, just about every household in southern Manitoba has received a fat flyer announcing Winkler's second January

MOONLIGHT SALE!

Open Til 11 p.m.!   First Come First Served!

Keep your eyes open to get the

FANTASTIC BUYS

BACON ENDS!   BANANAS!

19¢ lb.   9¢ lb. (6 p.m. to 9 p.m.)

Check These Hourly Specials!

Starting at 10 p.m. to 11 p.m.

Wide Angle

DUST PANS!

15 inches   Reg. 98¢

39¢ ea.

ALL ITEMS ARE AS STOCK LASTS!

The Moonlight Sale will be opened by a

Torchlight Parade of Snowmobiles

Down Winkler's Main Street at 7:00 p.m.

THURS. JAN. 20th

(Prices Good Only at Time Listed)

The temperature in Winkler at 7 p.m. on Thursday, January 20, 1972, is 35 below zero and dropping. The air is frozen into little slivers of glass which pierce the lungs. The light from the full moon reflected in the crystallized air makes the night fluorescent. People scurry through the neon streets beneath small white clouds of congealed breath like the balloons in comic strips. Tears run down their cheeks. The cold freezes

52

hands and feet to blocks of wood. It hurts to walk more than a few feet; even the cars scream and groan. The snowmobile parade has been cancelled because there's no snow.

Hundreds of cars begin to pour into Winkler just after suppertime, drawn like maggots to the smell of 20 per cent off. They come from all directions, strung out in long cavalcades, their lights visible on the highways for miles around, an encircling army on the march. Before 7 p.m. every parking space in Winkler is taken, not only on Main Street but on all the side streets for three and four blocks in every direction. All the church parking lots are full. The streets are choked with cars going round and round in hopeless circles, sending up blinding plumes of frozen exhaust which glow hellfire red from the brake lights. All the cars converge on the corner of Main Street and Mountain Avenue, Winkler's principal intersection, and create a monumental traffic jam, since Winkler's principal intersection, like all its other intersections, lacks a traffic light — a source of great humiliation to Winkler. Every car disgorges a horde of people swaddled in scarves, who run for the nearest store. They have waited a year for Winkler's Moonlight Sale and they're not going to miss it.

The stores are jammed. Knots of people spill out onto the sidewalks. They saunter casually from store to store as if it were a hot day in July and poke their heads in the windows of parked cars to say hello to the old women in babushkas huddled inside. Main Street is sunny, bathed in yellow lamplight streaming from the store windows; the headlights on the stalled cars make the street as bright as noon. The music store is piping cheerful accordion music into the street to entice people in towards the electric organs and color TVs. Even the Bible bookstore, which sells evangelical bumper stickers ("Have a Nice Eternity!"), is doing a thumping trade in sacred records and religious tracts.

The centre of excitement, and really the only reason for coming to Winkler, is Gladstone's store, a fabulous emporium of goods rescued from fire sales and bankruptcies across western Canada which takes up almost a full block on Main Street. Tension increases as 7:30 p.m. approaches, because that's the time of Gladstone's first Treasure Spot. The person standing closest to the hidden Treasure Spot receives his choice of any dress in the store for $1; if he has a Gladstone's sales slip for January 20, he gets another $25 worth of merchandise for another $1. The crowd in Gladstone's at 7:30 p.m. is so dense it's impossible to see who wins the Treasure Spot. The name of the winner is announced over the loud speaker; it's a man from a town 65 miles away.

People come at 7 p.m., because that's when apples go on sale for $2.09 a bushel and the Co-op has girls' blouses for 77 cents. But the featured items are cunningly spaced out to ensure that customers will spend as many hours as possible in Winkler. Pantyhose is 25 cents a pair at 8 p.m., but the orange juice doesn't go on sale until 9 p.m., and butter is cheap at 10 p.m. To save on all the specials a family has to spend between four and five hours in Winkler, and during that time, of course, they buy a whole lot of other stuff. The entranceways to the store are crammed with people standing guard over mounds of flour (100 pounds for $5.99), toilet paper, and tin cans. Waiting.

Eventually the crush pushes them out into the street, because in Winkler there's nowhere else to go. Winkler has a beer parlor, a dingy place in the old hotel still restricted to men only, and the Harvest Inn, a spartan arborite coffee shop. That's all. Squeezed out of the popular bargain basement stores, shoppers are forced to take refuge in the empty, higher-priced stores, much to the delight of the businessmen who are able to turn a 30-cent saving on a bag of bananas into an $800 three-room group.

The sale is joyless. Women paw desultorily through piles of cheap chiffon scarves and odd shoes and, frowning, burrow among the bruised tomatoes and the wilted lettuce. There is no shoving or pushing, no screaming or snatching or clawing, no bellows of anger or shrill arguments over merchandise. No laughter. Everyone is polite. People speak quietly in low voices, almost whispers. They stand patiently to be waited on, oblivious of the mob. In Penner's Dry Goods Store, where women have come for flannelette, the silence is almost reverent. It's a while before the low dull roar becomes noticeable. It's the steady oppressive sound of a million grasshoppers munching. Unsmiling, expressionless, methodical, the swarm of customers grinds its way through the store; they pick the shelves clean and devastate the fruit and vegetables. Some people have backed their cars and trucks up to the front door of Gladstone's grocery store; bent double like ants, they lug out bags of flour, cases of apples, and dozens of paper cartons full of groceries. They work with concentration, with passionate, single-minded intensity.

Shopping in Winkler is taken very seriously. There is nothing else to do. Winkler has no movies (movies are evil), no bars, no bowling alley, no clubs or lodges or fraternal organizations (except the Chamber of Commerce). Dancing is forbidden. Drinking is disapproved of. Sex is frowned upon. Shopping is recreation, an acceptable orgy. Women often apologize afterwards, saying, "Oh, I didn't really need anything, I just went for the outing."

Winkler is the Shopping Centre of Southern Manitoba. It's also one of the most religious towns in the province.

A CONVERSATION WITH MARIA, AN OJIBWAY GIRL
Joseph McLeod

Winnipeg
is cold
and windy
and flat
as a rock

If
you could
throw
Winnipeg
on top of Edmonton

pack
Prince Albert
under both

and
bunch
Calgary
around the edges

You
could have
one
Vancouver

THE GREAT ELECTRICAL REVOLUTION
Ken Mitchell

I was only a little guy in 1937, but I can still remember
Grandad being out of work. Nobody had any money to pay
him and as he said, there wasn't much future in brick-laying
as a charity. So mostly he just sat around in his suite above
the hardware store, listening to his radio. We *all* listened to it
when there was nothing else to do, which was most of the
time unless you happened to be going to school like me.
Grandad stuck right there through it all — soap operas,
weather reports, and quiz shows — unless he got a bit of cash
from somewhere. Then he and Uncle Fred would go downtown to the beer parlour at the King William Hotel.

Grandad and Grandma came from the old country long before I was born. When they arrived in Moose Jaw, all they had
was three children: Uncle Fred, Aunt Thecla, and my Dad; a
trunk full of working clothes; and a 26-pound post mall for
putting up fences to keep "rogues" off Grandad's land. Rogues
meant Indians, Orangemen, cattle rustlers, and capitalists. All
the way out on the train from Montreal, he glared out the
Pullman window at the endless flat, saying to his family:

"I came out here for land, b'Christ, and none of 'em's goin'
to sly it on me."

He had sworn to carve a mighty estate from the raw Sas-
katchewan prairie, although he had never so much as picked
up a garden hoe in his whole life before leaving Dublin.

So when he stepped off the train at the C.P.R. station in
Moose Jaw, it looked like he was thinking of tearing it down
and seeding the site to oats. It was two o'clock in the morning, but he kept striding up and down the lobby of the station, dressed in his good wool suit with the vest, as cocky as a
bantam rooster in a chicken run. My Dad and Uncle Fred and
Aunt Thecla sat on the trunk, while Grandma nagged at him
to go and find them a place to stay. (It was only later they
realized he was afraid to step outside the station.) He finally
quit strutting long enough to get a porter to carry their trunk
to a hotel down the street.

The next morning they went to the government land office to secure their homestead. Then Grandad rented a democrat and took my Dad and Uncle Fred out to see the land they had come half-way around the world to find. Grandma and Aunt Thecla were told to stay in the hotel room and thank the Blessed Virgin for deliverance. They were still offering their prayers some three hours later, when Grandad burst into the room, his eyes wild and his face pale and quivering.

"Sweet Jesus Christ!" he shouted at them. "There's too much of it! There's just too damn much of it out there." He ran around the room several times in circles, knocking against the walls. "Miles and miles of nothing but miles and miles!" He collapsed onto one of the beds, and lay staring at the ceiling.

"It 'ud drive us all witless in a week," he moaned.

The two boys came in and told the story of the expedition. Grandad had started out fine, perhaps just a little nervous. But the further they went from the town, the more agitated and wild-eyed he got. Soon he stopped urging the horse along and asked it to stop. They were barely ten miles from town when they turned around and came back, with Uncle Fred driving. Grandad could only crouch on the floor of the democrat, trying to hide from the enormous sky, and whispering hoarsely at Fred to go faster. He'd come four thousand miles to the wide open spaces — only to discover he suffered from agoraphobia.

That was his last real excursion onto the open prairie. He gave up forever the idea of a farm of his own. (He did make one special trip to Mortlach in 1928 to fix Aunt Thecla's chimney, but that was a family favour. Even then Uncle Fred had to drive him in an enclosed Ford sedan in the middle of the night, with newspapers taped to the windows so he couldn't see out.) There was nothing left for him to do but take up his old trade of brick-laying in the town of Moose Jaw, where there were trees and tall buildings to protect him from the vastness. Maybe it was a fortunate turn of fate; cer-

58

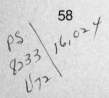

tainly he prospered from then until the Depression hit, about the time I was born.

Yet — Grandad always felt guilty about not settling on the land. Maybe it was his conscience that prompted him to send my Dad out to work for a cattle rancher in the hills, the day after he turned eighteen. Another point: he married Aunt Thecla off to a Lutheran wheat farmer at Mortlach who actually threshed about five hundred acres of wheat every fall. Uncle Fred was the eldest and closer to Grandad (he had worked with him as an apprentice brick-layer before they immigrated) so he stayed in town and lived in the suite above the hardware store.

I don't remember much about my father's cattle ranch, except whirls of dust and skinny animals dragging themselves from one side of the range to the other. Finally there were no more cattle, and no money to buy more, and nothing to feed them if we *did* buy them, except wild fox-tails and Russian thistles. So we moved into Moose Jaw with Grandad and Grandma, and went on relief. It was better than the ranch where there was nothing to do but watch tumbleweeds roll through the yard. We would have had to travel into town every week to collect the salted fish and government pork, anyway. Grandad was very happy to have us, because when my Dad went down to the railway yard to get our ration, he collected Grandad's too. My Dad never complained about waiting in line for the handout, but Grandad would've starved to death first. "The God-damned government drives us all to the edge," he would say. "Then they want us to queue up for the God-damned swill they're poisoning us with."

That was when we spent so much time listening to Grandad's radio. It came in a monstrous slab of black walnut cabinet he had swindled, so he thought, from a second-hand dealer on River Street. An incandescent green bulb glowed in the centre to show when the tubes were warming up. There was a row of knobs with elaborate-looking initials and a dial with the names of cities like Tokyo, Madrid, and Chicago.

Try as we might on long winter evenings to tune the needle into those stations and hear a play in Japanese or Russian, all we ever got was CHMJ Moose Jaw, The Buckle of the Wheat Belt. Even so, I spent hours lying on the floor, tracing the floral patterns on the cloth-covered speaker while I listened to another world of mystery and fascination.

When the time came that Grandad could find no more bricks to lay, he set a kitchen chair in front of the radio and stayed there, not moving except to go to the King William, where Uncle Fred now spent most of his time. My Dad had managed to get a job with the city, gravelling streets for fifty cents a day. But things grew worse. The Moose Jaw Light and Power Company 'came around one day in the fall of 1937 and cut off our electricity for non-payment. It was very hard on Grandad not to have his radio. Not only did he have nothing to do, but he had to spend all his time thinking about it. He stared out the parlour window, which looked over the alley running behind the hardware store. There was a grand view of the back of the Rainbow Laundry.

That was what he was doing the day of his discovery, just before Christmas. Uncle Fred and my Dad were arguing about who caused the Depression — R. B. Bennett or the C.P.R. Suddenly Grandad turned from the window. There was a new and strange look on his face.

"Where does that wire go?" he said.

"Wire?" said Uncle Fred, looking absent-mindedly around the room. He patted his pockets looking for a wire.

"What wire?" my Dad said.

Grandad nodded toward the window. "This wire running right past the window."

He pointed to a double strand of power line that ran from a pole in the back alley to the side of our building. It was a lead-in for the hardware store.

"Holy Moses Cousin Harry. Isn't that a sight now!" Grandad said, grinning like a crazy man.

"You're crazy," Uncle Fred told him. "You can't never get

a tap off that line there. They'd find you out in nothing flat."

Grandma, who always heard everything that was said, called from the kitchen: "Father, don't you go and do some foolishness will have us all electrinated."

"By God," he muttered. He never paid any attention to a word she said. "Cut off *my* power, will they?"

That night, after they made me go to bed, I listened to him and Uncle Fred banging and scraping as they bored a hole through the parlour wall. My Dad wouldn't have anything to do with it and took my mother to the free movie at the co-op. He said Grandad was descending to the level of the Moose Jaw Light and Power Company.

Actually, Grandad knew quite a bit about electricity. He had known for a long time how to jump a wire from one side of the meter around to the other, to cheat the power company. I had often watched him under the meter, stretched out from his tip-toes at the top of a broken step-ladder, yelling at Grandma to lift the God-damned Holy Candle a little higher so he could see what the Christ he was doing.

The next day, Grandad and Uncle Fred were acting like a couple of kids, snorting and giggling and jabbing each other in the ribs. They were waiting for the King William beer parlour to open so they could go down and tell their friends about Grandad's revenge on the power company. They spent the day like heroes down there, telling over and over how Grandad had spied the lead-in, and how they bored the hole in the wall, and how justice had finally descended on the capitalist leeches. The two of them showed up at home for supper, but as soon as they ate they headed back to the King William where everybody was buying them free beer.

Grandma didn't seem to think much of their efforts, although now that she had electricity again, she could spend the evenings doing her housework if she wanted to. The cord came through the hole in the wall, across the parlour to the hall and the kitchen. Along the way, other cords were attached which led to the two bedrooms. Grandma muttered when she had to sweep around the black tangle of wires and sockets. With six of us living in the tiny suite, somebody was forever tripping on one of the cords and knocking things over.

But we lived with all that because Grandad was happy again. We might *all* have lived happily if Grandad and Uncle Fred could have kept quiet about their revenge on the power company. One night about a week later we were in the parlour listening to Fibber McGee and Molly when somebody knocked at the door. It was Mrs. Pizak, who lived next door in a tiny room.

"Goot evening," she said, looking all around. "I see your power has turnt beck on."

"Ha," Grandad said. "We turned it on *for* 'em. Damned rogues."

"Come in and sit down and listen to the show with us," Grandma said. Mrs. Pizak kept looking at the black wires running back and forth across the parlour, and at Grandad's radio. You could tell she wasn't listening to the show.

"Dey shut off my power, too," she said. "I alvays like listen de Shut-In. Now my radio isn't vork."

"Hmmm," Grandad said, trying to hear Fibber and the Old-Timer. Grandma and my Dad watched him not listening to the radio any more either. Finally he couldn't stand it.

"All right, Fred," he said. "Go and get the brace and bit."

They bored a hole through one of the bedroom walls into Mrs. Pizak's cubicle. From then on, she was on Grandad's power grid, too. It didn't take long for everybody else in the block to find out about the free power, and they all wanted to hook up. There were two floors of suites above the hardware store, and soon the walls and ceiling of Grandad's suite were as full of holes as a colander, with wires running in all directions. For the price of a bottle of whiskey, people could run their lights twenty-four hours a day if they wanted. By Christmas Day, even those who *paid* their bills had given notice to the power company. It was a beautiful Christmas in a bad year — and Grandad and Uncle Fred liked to take a lot of credit for it. Nobody blamed them, either. There was a lot of celebration up and down the halls, where they always seemed to show up as guests of honour. There was a funny feeling running through the block, like being in a state of siege, or a revolution, with Uncle Fred and my Grandad leading it.

One late afternoon just before New Year's, I was lying on the floor of the front parlour, reading a second-hand Book of Knowledge I had got for Christmas. Grandma and my mother were knitting socks, and all three of us were listening vaguely to the Ted Mack Amateur Hour. Suddenly, out of the corner of my eye, I thought I saw Grandad's radio move. I blinked and stared at it, but the big console just sat there talking about Geritol. I turned a page. Again, it seemed to move in a jerk. What was going on?

"Grandma," I said. "The radio — "

She looked up from her knitting, already not believing a word I might have to say. I gave it up, and glared spitefully at the offending machine. While I watched, it slid at least six inches across the parlour floor.

"Grandma!" I screamed. "The radio's moving! It was sitting there — and it moved over here. All by itself!"

She looked calmly at the radio, then the tangle of wires spread across the floor, and out the front parlour window.

"Larry-boy, you'd best run and fetch your grandfather. He's over at McBrides'. Number eight."

McBrides' suite was down the gloomy hall and across. I dashed down the corridor and pounded frantically at the door. Someone opened it the width of a crack.

"Is my Grandad in there?" I squeaked. Grandad stepped out into the hall with a glass in his hand, closing the door behind him.

"What is it, Larry?"

"Grandma says for you to come quick. The radio! There's something — "

"My radio!" Grandad was not a large man, but he had the

energy of a buzz saw. He started walking back up the hall, breaking into a trot, then a steady gallop, holding his glass of whiskey out in front at arm's length so it wouldn't spill. He burst through the door and screeched to a stop in front of the radio, which sat there, perfectly normal except that it stood maybe a foot to the left of the chair.

"By the Holy toe-nails of Moses — what is it?"

Grandma looked up ominously and jerked her chin toward the window. Her quiet firmness usually managed to calm him, but now, in two fantastic bounds, Grandad stood in front of the window, looking out.

"Larry," he said, glaring outside, "fetch your Uncle Fred." I tore off down the hall again to number eight and brought Uncle Fred back to the suite. The two women were still knitting on the other side of the room. Grandma was doing her stitches calmly enough, but my mother's needles clattered like telegraph keys, and she was throwing terrified glances around the room.

"Have a gawk at this, will you, Fred?"

Uncle Fred and I crowded around him to see out. There, on a pole only twenty feet from our parlour window, practically facing us eye to eye, was a lineman from the power company. He was replacing broken glass insulators; God knows why he was doing it in the dead of winter. Obviously, he hadn't noticed our home-made lead-in, or he would have been knocking at the door. We could only pray he wouldn't look at the wire too closely. Once, he lifted his eyes toward the lighted window where we all stood gaping out at him in the growing darkness. He grinned at us, and raised his hand in a salute. He must have thought we were admiring his work.

"Wave back!" Grandad ordered. The three of us waved frantically at the lineman, to make him think we appreciated his efforts, although Grandad was muttering some very ugly things about the man's ancestry.

Finally, to our relief, the lineman finished his work and got ready to come down the pole. He reached out his hand for support — and my heart stopped beating as his weight hung on the contraband wire. Behind me, I could hear the radio slide another foot across the parlour floor. The lineman stared at the wire he held. He tugged experimentally, his eyes following it up to the hole through our wall. He looked at Grandad and Uncle Fred and me standing there in the lit-up window, with our crazy horror-struck grins and our arms frozen above our heads in grotesque waves. Understanding seemed to spread slowly across his face.

He scrambled around to the opposite side of the pole and braced himself to give a mighty pull on our line. Simultaneously, Grandad leaped into action, grabbing the wire on our side of the wall. He wrapped it around his hands, and braced his feet against the baseboard. The lineman gave his first vicious yank, and it almost jerked Grandad smack against the wall. I remember thinking what a powerful man the lineman must be to do that to my Grandad.

"Fred, you feather-brained idiot!" he shouted. "Get over here and haul on this line before the black-hearted son of a bitch pulls me through the wall."

Uncle Fred ran to the wire just in time, as the man on the pole gave another, mightier heave. At the window, I could see the lineman stiffen with rage and determination. The slender wire sawed back and forth through the hole in the wall for at least ten minutes, first one side, and then the other, getting advantage. The curses on our side got very loud and bitter. I couldn't hear the lineman, of course, but I could see him — with his mouth twisted in an awful snarl, throwing absolutely terrible looks at me in the window, and heaving on the line. I know he wasn't praying to St. Jude.

Grandad's cursing would subside periodically when Grandma warned: "Now, now, father, not in front of the boy." Then she would go back to her knitting and pretend the whole thing wasn't happening, as Grandad's violent language would soar to a new high.

That lineman must have been in extra-good condition, be-

cause our side very quickly began to play out. Grandad
screamed at Grandma and my mother, and even at me, to
throw ourselves on the line and help. But the women refused
to leave their knitting, and they wouldn't let me be corrupted.
I couldn't leave my viewpoint at the window, anyway.

Grandad and Uncle Fred kept losing acreage. Gradually the
huge radio had scraped all the way across the floor and stood
at their backs, hampering their efforts.

"Larry!" Grandad shouted. "Is he weakenin' any?"

He wanted desperately for me to say yes, but it was useless.
"It doesn't look like it," I said. Grandad burst out in a froth
of curses I'd never heard before. A fresh attack on the line
pulled his knuckles to the wall and barked them badly. He
looked tired and beaten. All the slack in the line was taken up
and he was against the wall, his head twisted looking at me.
A light flared up in his eyes.

"All right, Fred," he said. "If he wants the God-damned
thing so bad—let him have it!" They both jumped back—
and nothing happened.

I could see the lineman, completely unaware of his impend-
ing disaster, almost literally winding himself up for an all-out
assault on our wire. I wanted out of human kindness to shout
a warning at him. But it was too late. With an incredible
backward lunge, he disappeared from sight behind the power
pole.

A shattering explosion of wild noises blasted my senses, like
a bomb had fallen in Grandad's suite. Every appliance and
electric light that Grandma owned flew into the parlour,
bounding off the walls and smashing against each other. A
table lamp from the bedroom caromed off Uncle Fred's knee.
The radio collided against the wall and was ripped off its wire
by the impact. Sparking and flashing like lightning, all of
Grandma's things hurled themselves against the parlour wall.
They were stripped like chokecherries from an electric vine as
it went zipping through the hole. A silence fell—like a

breath of air to a drowning man. The late afternoon darkness settled through the room.

"Sweet Jesus Christ!" Grandad said. He had barely got it out, when there came a second uproar: a blood-curdling barrage of bangs and shouts, as our neighbours in the block saw all their lamps, radios, irons, and toasters leap from their tables and collect in ruined piles of junk around the "free power" holes in their walls. Uncle Fred turned white as a sheet.

I looked out the window. The lineman sat on the ground at the foot of his pole, dazed. He looked up at me with one more hate-filled glare, then deliberately snipped our wire with a pair of cutters. He taped up the end and marched away into the night.

Grandad stood in the midst of the ruined parlour, trying in the darkness to examine his beloved radio for damage. Grandma sat in her rocking chair, knitting socks and refusing to acknowledge the disaster.

It was Grandad who finally spoke first. "They're lucky," he said. "It's just God-damned lucky for them they didn't scratch my radio."

MY FRIEND THE REPORTER
Stephen Leacock

He came up to me on the platform just after I had finished giving my address, his notebook open in his hand.

"Would you mind," he said, "just telling me the main points of your speech? I didn't get to hear it."

"You weren't at the lecture?"

"No," he answered, pausing to sharpen his pencil, "I was at the hockey game."

"Reporting it?"

"No, I don't report that sort of thing. I only do the lectures and the highbrow stuff. Say, it was a great game. What did you say the lecture was about?"

"It was called 'The Triumphal Progress of Science'."

"On science, eh?" he said, writing rapidly as he spoke.

"Yes," I answered, "on science."

He paused.

"How do you spell 'triumphal'," he asked; "is it a PH or an F?"

I told him.

"And now," he went on, "what was the principal idea, just the main thing, don't you know, of your address?"

"I was speaking," I said, "of our advanced knowledge of radiating emanations and the light it throws on the theory of atomic structure."

"Wait a minute," he said, "till I get that. Is it r-a-d-i-a-t-i-n-g? . . . the light it throws, eh? . . . good. . . . I guess I got that."

He prepared to shut his little book.

"Have you ever been here before?"

"No," I said, "it's my first time."

"Are you staying in the new hotel?"

"Yes."

"How do you like it?"

"It's very comfortable," I said.

He reopened his book and scribbled fast.

"Did you see the big new abattoir they are putting in?"

"No," I said, "I didn't hear of it."

"It's the third biggest north of Philadelphia. What do you think of it?"

"I didn't see it," I said.

He wrote a little and then paused.

"What do you think," he asked, "of this big mix-up in the city council?"

"I didn't hear of it," I said.

"Do you think that the aldermen are crooked?"

"I don't know anything about these aldermen," I said.

"No," he answered, "perhaps not, but wouldn't you think it likely that they'd be crooked?"

"They often are crooked enough," I admitted, "in fact, very often a pack of bums."

"Eh, what's that, a pack of bums? That's good, that's great" — he was all enthusiasm now — "that's the kind of stuff, you know, that our paper likes to get. You see, so often you go and take a lecture and there's nothing said at all — nothing like that, don't you see? And there's no way to make anything out of it. . . . But with this I can feature it up fine. 'A pack of bums!' Good. Do you suppose they took a pretty big graft out of building the abattoir?"

"I'm afraid," I said, "that I don't know anything about it."

"But, say," he pleaded, "you'd think it likely that they did?"

"No, no," I repeated, "I don't know anything about it."

"All right," he said reluctantly, "I guess I'll have to leave that out. Well, much obliged. I hope you come again. Good night."

And the next morning as I was borne away from that city in the train I read his report in the paper, headed up with appropriate capitals and subheadings:

THINKS ALDERMEN PACK OF BUMS
Distinguished Lecturer Talks on Christian Science

"The distinguished visitor," so ran his report, "gave an interesting talk on Christian Science in the auditorium of the Y.M.C.A. before a capacity audience. He said that we were living in an age of radio and that in his opinion the aldermen of the city were a pack of bums. The lecturer discussed very fully the structure of anatomy which he said had emanated out of radio. He expressed his desire to hazard no opinion about the question of graft in regard to the new abattoir which he considers the finest that he has seen at any of his lectures. The address, which was freely punctuated with applause, was followed with keen attention, and the wish was freely expressed at the close that the lecturer might give it in other cities."

There! That's the way he does it, as all of us who deal with him are only too well aware.

And am I resentful? I should say not. Didn't he say that there was a "capacity audience" when really there were only sixty-eight people; didn't he "punctuate the lecture with applause", and animate it with "keen attention"? . . . What more can a lecturer want? And as to the aldermen and the graft and the heading up, that's our fault, not his. We want that sort of thing in our morning paper, and he gives it to us.

And with it, as his own share, a broad and kindly human indifference that never means to offend.

Let him trudge off into the night with his little book and pencil and his uncomplaining industry and take my blessing with him.

CALAMITY
F. R. Scott

A laundry truck
Rolled down the hill
And crashed into my maple tree.
It was a truly North American calamity.
Three cans of beer fell out
(Which in itself was revealing)
And a jumble of skirts and shirts
Spilled onto the ploughed grass.
Dogs barked, and the children
Sprouted like dandelions on my lawn.
Normally we do not speak to one another on this avenue,
But the excitement made us suddenly neighbours.
People exchanged remarks
Who had never been introduced
And for a while we were quite human.
Then the policeman came —
Sedately, for this was Westmount —
And carefully took down all names and numbers.
The towing truck soon followed,
Order was restored.
The starch came raining down.

GREETINGS
Lawren Harris

The other day
Walking along the street
I heard a man singing
High in the air
Above my head —
I looked up
And saw a lineman
Atop a telephone pole
Spiking on cross ties
To the rhythm of his song —
I smiled and said
"That's the stuff"
And he smiled back
And told me
To go to hell
As a man will
When he understands another.

AUTOBIOGRAPHICAL
A. M. Klein

Out of the ghetto streets where a Jewboy
Dreamed pavement into pleasant Bible-land,
Out of the Yiddish slums where childhood met
The friendly beard, the loutish Sabbath-goy,
Or followed, proud, the Torah-escorting band,
Out of the jargoning city I regret,
Rise memories, like sparrows rising from
The gutter-scattered oats,
Like sadness sweet of synagogal hum,
Like Hebrew violins
Sobbing delight upon their Eastern notes.

Again they ring their little bells, those doors
Deemed by the tender-year'd, magnificent:
Old Ashkenazi's cellar, sharp with spice;
The widows' double-parloured candy-stores
And nuggets sweet bought for one sweaty cent;
The warm fresh-smelling bakery, its pies,
Its cakes, its navel'd bellies of black bread;
The lintels candy-poled
Of barber-shop, bright-bottled, green, blue, red;
And fruit-stall piled, exotic,
And the big synagogue door, with letters of gold.

Again my kindergarten home is full —
Saturday night — with kin and compatriot:
My brothers playing Russian card-games; my
Mirroring sisters looking beautiful,
Humming the evening's imminent fox-trot;
My uncle Mayer, of blessed memory,
Still murmuring maariv, counting holy words;
And the two strangers, come
Fiery from Volhynia's murderous hordes —
The cards and humming stop.
And I too swear revenge for that pogrom.

Occasions dear: the four-legged aleph named
And angel pennies dropping on my book;
The rabbi patting a coming scholar-head;
My mother, blessing candles, Sabbath-flamed,
Queenly in her Warsovian perruque;
My father pickabacking me to bed
To tell tall tales about the Baal Shem Tov —
Letting me curl his beard.
Oh memory of unsurpassing love,
Love leading a brave child
Through childhood's ogred corridors, unfear'd!

The week in the country at my brother's — (May
He own fat cattle in the fields of heaven!)
Its picking of strawberries from grassy ditch,
Its odour of dogrose and of yellowing hay —
Dusty, adventurous, sunny days, all seven! —
Still follow me, still warm me, still are rich
With the cow-tinkling peace of pastureland.
The meadow'd memory
Is sodded with its clover, and is spanned
By that same pillow'd sky
A boy on his back one day watched enviously.

And paved again the street: the shouting boys,
Oblivious of mothers on the stoops,
Playing the robust robbers and police,
The corncob battle — all high-spirited noise
Competitive among the lot-drawn groups.
Another day, of shaken apple trees
In the rich suburbs, and a furious dog,
And guilty boys in flight;
Hazelnut games, and games in the synagogue —
The burrs, the Haman rattle,
The Torah dance on Simchas Torah night.

Immortal days of the picture calendar
Dear to me always with the virgin joy
Of the first flowering of senses five,
Discovering birds, or textures, or a star,
Or tastes sweet, sour, acid, those that cloy;
And perfumes. Never was I more alive.
All days thereafter are a dying off,
A wandering away
From home and the familiar. The years doff
Their innocence.
No other day is ever like that day.

I am no old man fatuously intent
On memoirs, but in memory I seek
The strength and vividness of nonage days,
Not tranquil recollection of event.
It is a fabled city that I seek;
It stands in Space's vapours and Time's haze;
Thence comes my sadness in remembered joy
Constrictive of the throat;
Thence do I hear, as heard by a Jewboy,
The Hebrew violins,
Delighting in the sobbed Oriental note.

FOG
Ethel Wilson

For seven days fog settled down upon Vancouver. It crept in
from the ocean, advancing in its mysterious way in billowing
banks which swallowed up the land. In the Bay and the Inlet
and False Creek, agitated voices spoke to one another. Small
tugs that were waylaid in the blankets of fog cried shrilly and
sharply "Keep away! Keep away! I am here!" Fishing-boats lay
inshore. Large freighters mooed continuously like monstrous
cows. The foghorns at Point Atkinson and the Lions' Gate
Bridge kept up their bellowings. Sometimes the fog quenched
the sounds, sometimes the sounds were loud and near. If there
had not been this continuous dense fog, all the piping and
boo-hooing would have held a kind of beauty; but it signified
danger and warning. People knew that when the fog lifted
they would see great freighters looking disproportionately large
riding at anchor in the Bay because passage through the Nar-
rows into the harbour was not safe. Within the harbour, laden
ships could not depart but remained lying fog-bound at great
expense in the stream . . . booo . . . booo . . . they warned. "I
am here! Keep away!" All the ships listened. The CPR boat
from Victoria crashed into the dock. Gulls collided in the
pathless air. Water traffic ceased and there was no movement
anywhere offshore.

In the streets, cars crawled slowly. Drivers peered. Pedes-
trians emerged and vanished like smoke. Up the draw of False
Creek, fog packed thick on the bridges. Planes were grounded.
People cancelled parties. Everyone arrived late for everything.

Mrs. Bylow was an old woman who lived in a small old
house which was more cabin than cottage in an unpleasant
part of Mount Pleasant. For the fifth day she sat beside her
window looking into the fog and cracking her knuckles because she had nothing else to do. If she had owned a telephone
she would have talked all day for pastime, repeating herself
and driving the party line mad.

Mrs. Bylow frequently sat alone and lonely. Her diurnal oc-
cupations had narrowed down to sleeping, waking to still

another day, getting up, making and swallowing small meals, belching a little, cleaning up (a little), hoping, going to the bathroom, going to the Chinaman's corner store, reading the paper (and thank God for that, especially the advertisements), becoming suddenly aware again of the noise of the radio (and thank God for that, too), and forgetting again.

This, and not much more, was her life as she waited for the great dustman and the ultimate box. So Mrs. Bylow's days and months slid and slid away while age — taking advantage of her solitariness, her long unemployment of vestigial brain, her unawareness of a world beyond herself, her absence of preparation for the grey years — closed down upon her like a vice, no, more like a fog. There had been a time about ten years ago when Mrs. Bylow, sitting on her small porch, beckoned to the little neighbour children who played on the sidewalk. "Come," said Mrs. Bylow, smiling and nodding.

The children came, and they all went into the kitchen. There was Mrs. Bylow's batch of fresh cookies and the children ate, looking around them, rapacious. They ate and ran away and once or twice a child hovered and said "Thank you." Perhaps that was not the child who said "Thank you", but parents speaking through the child ("Say Thank you to Mrs. Bylow!") so the child said "Thank you" and Mrs. Bylow was pleased. Sometimes the children lingered around the little porch, not hungry, but happy, noisy and greedy. Then Mrs. Bylow rejoiced at the tokens of love and took the children into the kitchen. But perhaps she had only apples and the children did not care for apples. "Haven't you got any cookies?" asked a bold one, "we got lotsa apples at home."

"You come Tuesday," said Mrs. Bylow, nodding and smiling, but the children forgot.

So within Mrs. Bylow these small rainbows of life (children, cookies, laughing, and beckoning (faded, although two neighbours did sometimes stop on their way home and talk for a few minutes and thus light up her day. Miss Casey who worked at the People's Friendly Market and was a smart dresser with fine red hair, and Mrs. Merkle who was the managing type and had eyes like marbles and was President of the Ladies' Bowling Club dropped in from time to time and told Mrs. Bylow all about the illnesses of the neighbours which Mrs. Bylow enjoyed very much and could think about later. Mrs. Merkle told her about Mr. Galloway's broken hip and Miss Casey told her about her mother's diabetes and how she managed her injections, also about the woman who worked in her department when she didn't need to work and how her kid had gone wrong and was in the Juvenile Court. Mrs. Bylow was regaled by everything depressing that her two friends could assemble because she enjoyed bad news which was displayed to her chiefly against the backdrop of her own experience and old age. All these ailments, recalling memories of her own (" . . . well I remember my Uncle Ernest's . . . "), provided a drama, as did the neglect and irresponsibility of the young generations. Like an old sad avid stupid judge she sat, passing judgement without ill will. It is not hard to understand why Mrs. Merkle and Miss Casey, hastening past Mrs. Bylow's gate which swung on old hinges, often looked straight ahead, walking faster and thinking I *must* go in and see her tomorrow.

During long periods of bad weather, as now in this unconquerable fog, time was a deep pit for Mrs. Bylow. Her hip was not very good. She should have belonged to a church (to such base uses can the humble and glorious act of worship come) or a club, to which she would at least look forward. Gone were the simple impossible joys of going to town, wandering through the shops, fingering and comparing cloth, cotton, and silk. Gone was the joy of the running children. Life, which had been pinkish and bluish, was grey. And now this fog.

So it was that on the fifth day of fog, Mrs. Bylow sat beside her window in a sort of closed-up dry well of boredom, cracking her knuckles and looking into the relentless blank that pressed against her window panes and kept her from seeing any movement on the sidewalk. Mrs. Merkle and Miss Casey were as though they had never been. I'm not surprised they wouldn't drop in, thought Mrs. Bylow modestly and without rancour, it couldn't be expected, it'll be all they can do to get home; and she pictured Miss Casey, with her flaming hair, wearing her leopard coat, pushing through the fog home to her mother. Diabetes, thought Mrs. Bylow, and she was sorry for old Mrs. Casey. Her indulgence of sorrow spread to include Miss Casey hurrying home looking so smart. Not much in life for her, now, is there, really, she thought, rocking. Mrs. Bylow peered again. She was insulted by this everywhere fog, this preventing fog. She needed a cup of cocoa and she had no cocoa. She repeated aloud a useful phrase, "The fog is lifting"; but the fog was not lifting.

Mrs. Bylow creaked to her feet. She wrapped herself up well, took her walking stick, and went unsteadily down her three steps. Then, not at all afraid, she turned to the left and, in a silence of velvet, she moved slowly along beside the picket fence which would guide her to Wong Kee's store. At her own corner a suggestion of sickly glow in the air told her that the street lamps were lighted. She moved on, screwing up her eyes against the greyish, yellow fog that invaded eyes, nose, mouth. At last another pale high glimmer informed her that she was near Wong Kee's store and, gasping, leaning now and then against the outside wall of the store itself, she reached the door with the comfortable knowledge that, once inside, she would find light and warmth. She would ask Wong Kee for his chair or a box and would sit down and take her ease while the Chinaman went with shuffling steps to the shelf where he kept the tins of cocoa. Wong Kee was a charming old man with good cheek-bones and a sudden tired Oriental smile. After Mrs. Merkle and Miss Casey he was Mrs. Bylow's third friend. She pushed the door open and waddled in to where there was this desired light and warmth, puffing a little.

Something was happening inside the store, a small whirlwind and fury. Mrs. Bylow was roughly pushed by large rushing objects. She lost her balance and was thrown, no, hurled violently to the ground. The person or persons rushed on, out and into the fog. The door slammed.

The store was empty. Everything was still. The old woman lay in a heap, bewildered and in pain. Gradually she began to know that someone or some people had rushed out into the fog, knocking her down and hurting her because she happened to be in the way. She whimpered and she thought badly of Wong Kee because he did not come to help her. Her body gave her massive pain, and as she looked slowly about her in a stupefied way she saw that a number of heavy cans of food had rained down upon her and lay around her. As she tried clumsily to heave herself up (but that was not possible), a customer came in.

"Well well well!" said the customer bending over her, "whatever . . ." then he straightened himself and listened.

A faint sound as of a bubbling sigh came from behind the counter on which was the till. The till was open and empty. The customer went behind the counter and again bent down. Then he drew himself up quickly. Wong Kee lay like a bundle of old clothes from which blood seeped and spread. The sound that the customer had heard was the soft sound of the death of Wong Kee who was an honest man and innocent. He had worked all his life and had robbed no one. He had an old wife who loved him. In a way hard to explain they were seriously and simply happy together. This was now over.

The customer paid no further attention to Mrs. Bylow on the floor but, stepping round Wong Kee's body, reached the telephone.

A small woman parted the dingy curtains which separated the store from the home of Wong Kee and his wife. She held in her arms a bundle of stove wood and stood motionless like a wrinkled doll. Then the stove wood clattered to the ground and she dropped to her knees uttering high babbling noises. She rocked and prostrated herself beside the impossible sight of her husband's dead body and his blood. The customer regarded her as he talked into the telephone. Then he too knelt down and put his arm round her. He could find nothing to say but the immemorial "There there . . . ."

Mrs. Bylow, lying neglected on the floor, endeavoured to look behind her but she had to realize as people do in bombardment, flood, and earthquake that she was at the mercy of whatever should happen to her and could not do anything about it, let alone look behind her.

"They're slow coming," said the customer. "It's the fog."

The old Chinese woman wrenched herself from him. "I tarryphome," she cried out, "I tarryphome my son . . . ."

The door opened and there seemed to be some policemen. The outside fog poured in with this entrance and some other kind of fog pressed down upon Mrs. Bylow's understanding and blurred it. "I'm a very old woman," she mumbled to a constable who had a little book, "and they knocked me down . . . they mighta killed me . . . they shouldn't a done that . . . they've broke my hip . . . aah . . . !"

"Yes lady, we'll look after you," said the constable, "who was it?"

"It was . . ." (well, who was it?) "I guess it was some man . . . no . . ." she breathed with difficulty, she should not have to suffer so, "I guess it was a boy . . . no, two boys . . . they knocked me down . . . ."

A constable at the door said to a crowd which had gathered from somewhere in the fog and now pushed against the front of the store, "Now then, you can't come in here, there's been a robbery, see? You best go on home," but someone battered on the pane with both hands enough to break it, and Miss Casey burst in at the door, her red hair wet with fog.

"She's here! Yes there she is!" said Miss Casey talking to everyone in her loud voice and bringing into the muted shop a blazing of bright eyes and hair and leopard coat and humanity, " — that's what I thought! I thought right after I left the store I'd better go in and see was she O.K. because she

shouldn't be out and the fog was just *awful* and I prett' near
went past her gate but I kinda felt something was wrong and
my goodness see what happened . . . . Mrs. Bylow honey,
what happened you," and Miss Casey dropped on her knees
and took Mrs. Bylow's hand in hers. "Say, what's been going
on around here, anyway?" she said, looking up at the constable ready to accuse.

"She's not so good," said the constable in a low tone in
Mrs. Bylow's dream and a high noise came into the night
("That's the syreen," said Miss Casey) and some men lifted her
and took her somewhere on a bed. It did not occur to Mrs.
Bylow that perhaps she had been killed inadvertently by two
youths who had just killed her old friend, but if a policeman
had said to her, "Now you are dead," she would have accepted
the information, so unfamiliar was the experience of boring
horizontally through a fog at top speed very slowly in a high
and unexplained swelling noise. She opened her eyes and saw a
piece of Miss Casey's leopard coat and so she was not dead.

"Is it reel?" she whispered, because she had always wanted
to know.

"Is what reel?" said Miss Casey bending her flaming head.
"Sure it's reel. The collar's reel anyway." Mrs. Bylow closed
her eyes again for several years and said, "But I never got my
cocoa." Then she began to cry quietly because she felt old and
helpless and the pain was something cruel but it was good to
feel Miss Casey beside her in her leopard coat. She did not
know that Wong Kee was dead — slugged on the head,
pistol-whipped, stabbed again and again in the stomach with a
long knife — all because he had summoned his small strength
and fought like a cat and defended himself for his right to his
thirty dollars and some loose change and a handful of cigarettes and his life. "Well, here we are," said Miss Casey, standing up, very cheerful.

In a week or two, while she was better and before she got
worse, Mrs. Bylow began to remember the two boys whom

she had never seen and, as she constructed their leather jackets and their faces, she said she would know them anywhere. Of course she would not, and the murderers of Wong Kee were never found but carried the knowledge of their murder into the fog with them on their way from the betrayal of their youth to whatever else they would soon violently undertake to do. When they arrived back, each at his own home, their parents said in pursuance of their habit of long years past, "Where you bin?" and the hoodlums said in pursuance of their habit of long years past, "Out." This satisfied the idiot parents. They said, "My that fog's just terrible," and the hoodlums said, "Sure is." They were excited and nervous because this was the first time they had killed, but they had the money. One of the young hoodlums did not go into the room where his parents were but went upstairs because he was pretty sure there was still some blood on his hands and so there was. Wong Kee's blood was on his parents' hands too but they, being irresponsible, did not know this. And on their hands was the blood of Mrs. Bylow who was soon to die, and of Mrs. Wong Kee who could no longer be said to live, and of their own hoodlum children.

Before Mrs. Bylow died, wiped out by forces quite outside herself like a moth in a storm (not much more and no less), she began to be a little proud of almost being present at a murder.

"It's not everyone who's been at a murder, Miss Casey, love, is it?"

"No honey," said Miss Casey, seeing again that sordid scene, "it isn't everyone."

"I always liked that coat of yours," said Mrs. Bylow.

"And then," said Miss Casey to Mrs. Merkle, "d'you know what she said? She said if ever I come to die — just like she wasn't ever going to — would you please wear your leopard coat. She's crazy about that coat. And then she said she often thought of those two boys that killed the storekeeper and

knocked her down and she guessed it was more their parents'
fault and not their fault. It made the tears come to your eyes,"
said Miss Casey who was kind as well as noisy and cherished a
sense of personal drama.

"Sure," said Mrs. Merkle who had eyes like marbles that
did not weep.

Mrs. Bylow's death was obscure and pitiful. Miss Casey got
the afternoon off and so there were two people at her funeral.
Miss Casey wore her leopard coat as promised.

YONGE STREET SATURDAY NIGHT
Raymond Souster

Except when the theatre crowds engulf the sidewalks
at nine, at eleven-thirty,
this street is lonely, a thousand lights in a thousand
     shop-windows
will not break her lips into a smile.

There are a few bums out,
there are lovers with hands held tightly,
there are the drunk ones, but they are princes among men,
     and are few,
and there are some like us,
just walking, making our feet move ahead of us,
a little bored, a little lost, a little angry,
walking as though we were really going somewhere,
walking as if there was something to see at Adelaide or
     maybe on King,
something that will give a fair return for this use of
     shoe-leather,
something that will make us smile with a strange new
     happiness, a lost but recovered joy.

REQUIEM FOR BIBUL
Jack Ludwig

Once upon a time — if we counted time not by calendars but
by assimilated history and scientific change I'd be tempted to
say four or five thousand years ago: before total war and all-out
war, before death camps, Nagasaki, before fusion and fission,
jets, moon shots, cosmonauts, Luniks in orbit, before antibio-
tics, polio vaccine, open-heart surgery, before TV, carburetors,
and other wonders of automation, before dead-faced hoods on
motorcycles, dead-faced beatniks on maldecycles — once upon
that kind of time lived a boy and his horse.

The year was 1939. This is no pastoral tale. The boy and
the horse are both dead.

Twenty years late, counting time by the calendar, I write
you of this boy Bibul and his horse Malkeh, of Bibul's ambi-
tion and his sad, sad end. In time-sorrowed perspective I record for you the imprint Bibul left on my mind and feeling
— his ticlike blink, his coal-black hair in bangs over his
forehead, his emery-cloth shaver's shadow, his ink-stained
mouth, his immutable clothes that wouldn't conform to style
or the seasons: always black denim Relief-style pants whitened
by wear and washing, always a brown pebbled cardigan coiled
at the wrists and elbows with unraveled wool, always a leather
cap with bent visor, split seams, matching the color and tex-
ture of Bibul's hair. And old ruined Malkeh, scorned before
lamented, making her daily round under Bibul's urging, dragging his creak of a fruit-peddler's wagon through Winnipeg's
"island" slum north of the Canadian Pacific Railway Yards.

Bibul peddled while my time burned: in 1939 all of us
high-school boys, owlish with sixteen- and seventeen-year-old
speculation, almost missed seeing this Bibul foxy with
world-weary finagling. We were out to save the world, Bibul
a buck. Hip deep in reality, trying to beat tricky suppliers,
weasely competitors, haggling customers, Bibul couldn't believe in us vaguesters. Peddling had forced him to see, hear,
and judge everything. By his practical measure we were simply
unreal. We'd speculate; Bibul would respond with *yeh-yeh*

— the Yiddish double affirmative that makes a negative. He didn't have to say a word, or raise a sceptical eyebrow, or even frown with that tic. His smell alone argued a reality out of reach of our politely neutral Lux, Lifebuoy, Vitalis middle-class sweetness: "effluvium Bibul" we called that mixture of squashed berries, bad turnips, dank pineapple crates, straw, chickens, sad old horsey Malkeh. Bibul had a grand gesture to sweep away our irrelevance, a sudden movement of the hand like a farmwife's throwing feed to chickens, his nose sniffing disgust, his sour mouth giving out a squelching sound, *aaaa*. Sometimes he sounded like a goat, other times a baby lamb — just *aaaa*, but enough to murder our pushy pretentions.

We were a roomful of competitive sharks — math sharks, physics sharks, English, Latin, history sharks — secretly, often openly, sure we surpassed our teachers in brains and know-how. Joyfully arrogant we shook off the restricting label of high-school student, considering ourselves pros — mathematicians, scientists, writers, artists. In our own minds we had already graduated from the university, had passed through Toronto or Oxford, were entangled in public controversies with the great names in our respective fields, ending right but humble, modestly triumphant. But where was Bibul in this league? As loud as we pros hollered Bibul heard nothing. He only yawned, slouched, even snoozed, gave out with that killing *yeh-yeh*, poked his grayish nose into his peddler's notebook red with reality's ooze of tomato.

"Bibul," we'd say in the break between classes, "do semantics mean nothing to your knucklehead? An intellectual revolution's coming. You've got to stand up and be counted. What'll it be? Are you *for* Count Korzybski or against him?"

"Aaaa," *aa*ed Bibul, and his chicken-feeding motion sent us back to ivory towers.

"You nuddin' bud gids," he'd say haughtily whenever we disturbed his audit of fruit-and-vegetable reality. "A 'ell of a lod you guys know aboud live."

Though we jeered and mocked, treated him like a clown, he was one of us, so how could we disown him? Kings of St.

John's High, lording it from our third-floor eminence over the giants and dwarfs living the underground life in the school's basement ascreech with whirling lathes and milling machines, or those second-floor, salt-of-the-earth commercial students dedicated to bookkeeping, typing, the sensible life, we of course wanted to pass our nobility on to Bibul. We ran the yearbook and could have established him there, but on the "island" English ran a poor second to Ukrainian, Polish, German, or in his case, Hebrew. We could have made him captain of the debating team, but peddling wrecked that; wrought up he stammered, angry he slobbered — no way to win arguments. Being a businessman, like his breed he had no time for politics; being tone-deaf he was a flop at glee-club try-outs. At sports he was dreadful. He couldn't swim a stroke, or skate, was flubby-knuckled at baseball, slashingly pigeon-toed at soccer, truly kamikaze going over a hurdle. And women? He had no time for them in his practical life; his old mare Malkeh and the ladies who haggled with him were the only females Bibul knew.

In recognition of his memo-book involvement we made Bibul our room treasurer.

After classes we theoreticians sprawled on the school green and took pleasure from long-limbed, heavy-thighed, large-breasted girls thwarting an educator's pious wish that the serge tunic neutralize the female form. Bibul was never with us. At the closing bell he'd run off to his horse and wagon, set to run the gauntlet of his customers (*shnorrers,* pigs, he called them); and early on a morning, when we theoreticians-turned-lovers, weary after a long night of girl-gaming, sat in Street Railway waiting houses knocking ourselves out over a noisy reading of Panurge's adventure with the Lady of Paris, Bibul, up and dressed since 4:00 A.M., struggled at the Fruit Row for bruised fruit and battered vegetables in competition with wizened peddlers and their muscular sons.

Lost in abstraction — and me, I thought little of Bibul in those days. He was a clown. A mark. A butt. The peddling was part of the sad, desperate struggle for money every family in the Depression knew. Bibul was the eldest of four children, his widowed ma supporting them on what she could make out of a tiny grocery store, doing the best she could, the dear lady, known throughout the "island" as "The Golden Thumb" and "The Adder", the latter reference ambiguous, meaning either snakes or computation, Bibul's ma being famous for a mathematical theorem that said $5 + 6 = 12$ or 13, whichever was higher.

Not till the year of our graduation did I discover why Bibul peddled with such dedication, why he rode out like a teen-age Don Quixote to do battle with those abusive, haggling, thieving *shnorrers*.

And what a riding-out that was! His paintless wagon listed like a sinking ship, sounded like resinless fiddles in the hands of apes, each wheel a circle successfully squared. Bibul sat on a tatter of leatherette bulging at the ends like a horsehair cream puff over his wilted greens and culled fruit. Bibul's faultless-in-his-favor scales made judgment, his battered tin scoop more dented than a tin BB target. And what was more fitting than a nag like Malkeh to drag that crumbling wagon on its progress?

As grim as Don Quixote's Rosinante would look next to elegant Pegasus, that's how Malkeh would have looked next to Rosinante; she was U-shaped in side view, as if permanently crippled by the world's fattest knight lugging the world's heaviest armor. She sagged like a collapsed sofa with stuffing hanging low. She was bare as buffed mohair, her shoulders tanned from the rub of reins, her color an unbelievable combination of rust, maroon, purple, bronze, found elsewhere only in ancient sun-drenched velvets. Her tail was a Gibson Girl's worn discarded feather boa, its fly-discouraging movements ritualistic, perfunctory, more to let flies know that Malkeh wasn't dead than that she was alive. Her legs, like a badly carpentered table, were of assorted lengths, which made Malkeh move by shuffling off like a pair of aged soft-shoe dancers in a final farewell. Her hooves were fringed with fuzzy hairs like a frayed fiddle bow abandoned to rain and sun, her horseshoes dime thin, rusty as the metal hinges on her wagon's tailgate. To encourage Malkeh to see, Bibul covered her almost-blind eyes with a pair of snappy black racing-horse blinkers trimmed with shiny silver rivets, a touch to her decor like a monocle in the eye of a Bowery bum.

Out of compassion, out of loyalty to this wreck of a horse, Bibul let his wagon go to ruin: wood could be camouflaged with paint or varnish but where was covering to hide or revive sad old mortal Malkeh?

One day I came to school early, and saw her.

She was the horse version of the "Dying Gaul". On Bibul's "island" Malkeh suffered no invidious comparisons, but on a main thoroughfare like St. John's High's Salter Street, Malkeh was exposed to the cruelty of horse hierarchy, and her submarginal subproletariat hide was bared. High-stepping, glossy-flanked, curried and combed T. Eaton Company horses, middle-class cousins of aristocratic thoroughbreds seen only on race tracks, veered their rumps sharply as they passed, hooves steel-ringing, traces white as snow. Their tails were prinked out with red ribbon, their wagons chariots sparkling in red, white, gold against blue-blackness that could mean only good taste. These bourgeois horses had the true bourgeois comforts — warm blankets, stables with hay wall to wall, feed bags that offered privacy and nourishment. Their drivers looked like sea captains — neat contrasts to a slop like Bibul. And their commercial feed was gastronomical compared with the bad lettuce, wilted carrot tops, shriveled beets Bibul shoved at Malkeh in a ripped old postman's pouch.

Malkeh took their snubs without flinching. It was part of the class struggle. What hurt was the heavy, powerful working-class Percherons and their stinking garbage scows when they avoided kinship with Malkeh, acting like a guest at a high-toned party ignoring a waiter who's a close relative.

Pity old Malkeh's vengeful heart; the only pleasure she got from her enforced station on Salter Street came from knowing flies used her as an aerodrome from which to launch vicious attacks on the elegant department-store horses passing.

I saw her. The principal, too, saw her, slouched with resignation, a "Don't" in an SPCA exhibit, her right foreleg flatteringly fettered by a cracked curling stone to give Malkeh the impression she had the vim and youth to turn runaway horse. Malkeh died a long time ago, but years before she did the principal had her one visit gnomically memorialized and graven in metal; early next morning, where Malkeh had stood, this marker went up: *No Parking at Any Time.*

Bibul never again brought her to school.

Which is not to say that life on the "island" was without its grim side; what accounted for an almost-blind horse wearing blinkers? *Shnorrers!* Those women with bare feet stuck hurriedly into their husbands' outsized felt slippers, their hair uncombed, faces unmade, women in nightgowns at four on a sunshiny afternoon, hands clenching pennies and silver Bibul had to charm away from them with hard-sell and soft-soap. Singly they waited, in concert plotted, en masse moved in on him. Their purpose was simple — *get much, pay little.* To the victor went Bibul's spoiled spoils.

"Giddy ahb, Malgeh," Bibul would holler from his high seat on the wagon, and his cry sounded to a *shnorrer's* ears like a warring clarion.

Into the lists Malkeh dragged the keening wagon, onto the "island" in ruins like a medieval town (Canadian history is short, but our buildings add spice by getting older faster). Foundationless hovels kids might have built out of assorted-sized decks of cards sagged, leaned at crazy-house angles to astound Pisa. Gates tipsy as Malkeh's wagon swung on one hinge from a last lost post; dry, cracking wood fences leaned in surrender toward the ground, begging like old men in sight of a grave to be allowed to fall the rest of the way; windows were tarpaper-patched, like pirates' eyes, ominous as the blackness left in the streets by uninsured fires.

Behind every window or screen opaque with dust, behind every door splintered from kids' kicking waited the *shnorrers*, trying to make Bibul anxious, make him sweat a little, a cinch for persistent hagglers.

"Ebbles, ebbles, den bondz f'a quadder," Bibul shouted.
Crafty with stealth the *schnorrers* didn't bite.

Unflustered, unfooled, Bibul took advantage of the phony
war, biting off the only three unspotted cherries in his entire
stock while Malkeh dragged the exposed tin rims of the wagon
wheels into the frost heaves and back-lane crevices. That
cramped, stinking back lane was mutually agreeable as a
Compleat Battlefield — for Bibul because the solid pall of
chicken droppings and horse dung was fine camouflage for the
imperfections Time and Decay wrought upon his produce, for
the *shnorrers* because the narrow quarters made tampering with
the scale easier, detection harder, filching a hot possibility.

"Whoa beg, whoa der, Malgeh," Bibul ordered, oblivious of
the spying women.

There, among rusted bedsprings hung up like huge harps,
torn mattresses resembling giant wads of steel wool, in a
boneyard of Model T's, Malkeh and the wagon rested. Dogs
scooted in darts of nervous yapping, cats hissed down from
rust-streaked corrugated rooftops, pigeons wheeled high above
Bibul's untroubled head, returning to perch on overhanging
eaves like fans anxious to get close to a scene of scuffle.

The *shnorrers* tried to read Bibul's face: the text was that
Sphinxlike tic of a blink. Stalling, he made entries into that
memo book, peeled an orange, scratched himself with casual
but maddening thoroughness.

The *shnorrers'* united front crumbled. A foot slipped out
from behind a door. Then a head.

"What you gonna cheat me on t'day, Bibul?" rasped out of
an impatient throat.

The war was on! Horseflies, the Depression having made
pickings so sparse they dropped their high standards and declared Malkeh a host, left the depressing fare of uncovered
garbage cans (each lid long ago commandeered to be target in
the minor-league jousts of the *shnorrers'* unknightly kids), and
hiding behind the *shnorrers* sneaking up to do Bibul battle,
launched assault on old Malkeh's flat weak flanks.

The siege began swiftly, deftly: a red-haired old woman

flipped two-cent oranges into the one-cent bins, her other hand pointing up at the sky to make Bibul raise his eyes and predict weather.

Her accomplice brought Bibul back to reality, picking the bargains up before they'd even stopped rolling.

"Boyaboy Bibul, you god good tings in y'usually stinkin' stock. Look here, Mrs. Gilfix, at such oranges."

Bibul's ticlike blink snapped like a camera shutter on their mischief.

"Give over here dem oniges," he reproved them. "*Yoysher*, show a liddle resdraind," and the sad old innocents watched the two-cent numbers fall back into the two-cent bins.

On the other side of the wagon a pair of raspberry hands crushed away at lettuce greens.

"Hom much off f' damaged goods?" the criminal hollered, wiping lettuce juice on her gaping nightgown.

But the red-haired old woman hadn't given up on oranges.

"Black head means black heart, robber," she cried out. "Perls, d'fruit man who has a white head and eight kids and supports two unmarried sisters in Russia, from *him* I get fresher cheaper by two coppers — ha come, ha? Ha come?"

"My oniges are Sundgizd, Blue Gooze," Bibul, a sucker for brand names, came back huffily. "Berls' oniges grow on ebble drees."

One man's quarrel is another woman's smoke screen. The *shnorrers* moved in, squeezing the fruit, poking, tapping, complaining with shrieks and curses that sent the pigeon-hearted pigeons high off their perches. Like a bucket brigade the ladies passed fruit up and down the length of the wagon, each nose an inspector, those with teeth taking their duties more seriously, tasters whose opinions Bibul could live without.

"*Shnorrers*, dad youz are," he hollered, holding up a nipped apple, a chewed-up orange. "You god no gare vor my brovids?"

"Look how he's independent," mocked the red-haired one, lunging fruitless after a fistful of cherries. "Look how he holds hisself big! His fadder's a doctor, maybe? Or the mayor?"

94

Bibul was a lone guard defending his fortress from desperate pillagers; ubiquitous as Churchill, many-handed as Shiva, he had to be compassionate as Schweitzer. Though *I* didn't know what Bibul's dedication to peddling was all about, the *shnorrers* did: Bibul was saving up to become a Rabbi. Bibul immersed himself in the practical, pedestrian, material life because of a Great Cause — the Yeshiva in New York, eventual immersion in a spiritual life dedicated to comfort suffering mankind.

How the *shnorrers* used that Great Cause in their war with Bibul! It was all double; in sincerity they poured out their hearts to him — an educated boy, soon to be a Rabbi, maybe he'd understand their side — the husband who had taken off and never come back, the bad-hearted rich relatives, the ungrateful kids, the treacherous friends, root, trunk, branch of a Jewish Seven Deadly Sins. They dizzied him with complicated stories, unsettled his strong stomach with demonstrations of human frailty — missing teeth, crossed eyes, wens, tumors, needed operations.

As a bonus to sincerity they hoped the tales would divert Bibul long enough for their aprons to fill with filched fruit.

Crying real tears Bibul would free an apricot from a fist already stained with cherry.

"A religious you call yourself?" the caught thief howled. "God should strike me dead if I stole ever in my life one thing!"

Glancing up at the sky she moved closer to the other ladies; who knew what kind of pull with God a boy-studying-to-be-a-Rabbi had?

"Bibul, sveedhard," cooed one Mrs. Itzcher, blemished but bleached, "give off ten cents a dozen by oranges and Tillie'll show plenty appreciation."

Bibul used his chicken-feed gesture to ward off temptation.

The *shnorrers* prayed God to give Bibul good enough ears to hear their laments but to compensate with a little dimming of the eyes so he wouldn't catch them stealing. When they lost they cursed in tones loud enough to be heard above the world's fishwifery in action.

No wonder Bibul considered us sharks irrelevant. After those *shnorrers* poured it on what was left to be said?

"My brudder's second wibe's kid wid da hump in back, Rabbi Bibul, has already her third miscarriage."

In the midst of haggle they rained down proofs of suffering and absurdity — banged heads, cut knees, singed eyelashes, hands caught in wringers, slippery floors, broken steps, toppling ladders. The compensation they asked was meager: pity, a buy on a busted watermelon.

When we sharks, hot for culture, cool for Schoenberg, long on judgments, short on facts, turned our abstract expressions Bibul's way how else could he respond but with that *aaaa*? What did our books and ideas have to compete with a *shnorrer*'s lament? Now when I think of that *aaaa* I translate it: "When I was a child I spake as a child . . ." (may Bibul forgive me for quoting St. Paul). *Aaaa* said, "Vanity of vanities, all is vanity," in explanation of the term for Mammon so that the rest would be with Abraham, Isaac, and Jacob. *Aaaa* said, "To everything there is a season, and a time to every purpose under the heaven."

On St. John's High School's Graduation Day Bibul was already at least half a Rabbi. The cardigan was gone, so too the denims and the black leather cap. He wore a fancy blue serge suit so new it still smelled of smoke. His sideburns were growing religiously into side curls, his emery-cloth shadow was now a beardlike reality. But it was Bibul's eyes I remember, excited, gay, snapping under that tic. He looked incredibly happy.

"Bibul," I said seriously, "you look beautiful in that suit!"

"Damorra, Joe," he said low and secretive, "damorra I go d'Noo Yorick an' d'Yeshiva."

I talked to him without clowning. He told me what he wanted, explained the peddling.

"Bibul," I said as we were walking out to our waiting parents, "doesn't the idea of a city the size of New York scare you? You'll be strange. Winnipeg's a village — "

"Wadz t'be asgared?" Bibul said with that wave of his hand. "Beoble iz beoble. I zeen all ginds aready."

He told me he'd sold Malkeh to Perls, the peddler. His mother walked proudly toward Bibul as we reached the street.

"Bibul," I shouted as parents came between us, "you'll be a terrific Rabbi! Good luck!"

He gave that chicken-feed flourish, but with new style, and with modesty.

"Aaaa," I heard above the shouting congratulations of parents, the last time I heard or saw Bibul.

That fall we sharks entered the university, and Canada the war. Winnipeg was transformed, full of aircrew trainees from places I knew about before only through postage stamps, men with yellow skins, red, brown, black, Maori tribesmen from New Zealand, bushmen from Australia, strange-sounding South Africans, carved-faced Indians thronging the streets and beer parlors. But far off in New York, Bibul, who had known war with the *shnorrers,* paid little attention to this latest struggle. He studied Torah and Talmud. He made his spending money selling fruit to Lower East Side *shnorrers* at the Essex Street Market.

Bibul's old Winnipeg customers haggled half-heartedly with old man Perls and old horse Malkeh, the one mercifully deaf, the other nearly blind. The Depression seemed over; money came easier.

Once in a long while I checked in at Bibul's mother's store, and gleaning news of Bibul, let her weigh me up a light pound of corned beef. She wore her hair Buster Brown, carried a huge buxom body on little feet in gray-white tennis shoes.

She shoved a letter at me.

"Look how a educated boy writes!" she said, pugnaciously proud. "Who but a Rabbi could understand such words?"

She pulled it back before I could answer.

"See him only, just look," she pushed a picture at my eyes.

Bibul huddled against a bare Williamsburg wall grinning the same grin as the three other Bibuls in the picture, all of them bearded and wild as Russians, in black beaver hats bought with money they had earned tutoring the Americanized grandchildren of rich Chassidim.

"Some boy, my Bibul," his mother called to me as I was leaving.

Winter passed and the war grew grimmer. Spring was beautiful, the war more dreadful. Summer was hot, particularly in New York, where Bibul divided his time between the Yeshiva and Essex Street's *shnorrers*. For days the temperature was in the high nineties. Bibul had never known such heat. He couldn't study, sleep, sell. In desperation he took himself one evening to the "Y", forgetting in the heat that he'd never learned to swim.

An attendant, going off duty, warned Bibul away, told him not to enter the pool. Who can be blind to Bibul's response?

"Aaaa," and that gesture.

He drowned.

His *shnorrers* on the "island", being told, wept and lamented. We sharks, even in the midst of war's casualties, were moved and stricken. Bibul was the first of us to die.

I cannot find Bibul's like in Winnipeg today.

Somebody waved a T-square wand over the old "island", bringing in the ninety-degree angle unknown in Bibul's far-off day. Progress pretends Bibul's "island" never really existed; the lanes are paved, the rotten wood of wall and fence has been sloshed over with paint. A few sneaky signs of the old world are around: a clothesline pole, exhausted from long years of soggy fleece-lined underwear to support, seems ready to give up the ghost; an outside staircase, impermanent as a hangman's scaffold, mocks the fire commission that asked for greater safety and got greater danger.

Malkeh is dead. The wagon is all bits and crumble.

Motorized peddlers in trucks like Brink's Cars zoom through the reformed "island" late at night with the remnants of produce picked over by ringed and braceleted hands on the day route — River Heights, Silver Heights, Garden City, places of Togetherness, Betterness, Spotlessness, the polite answers Comfort has given to the sad old questions of Civilization.

"Apples, apples, two pounds for a quarter," the peddlers call, but not too loudly, and the women once poor enough to be *shnorrers* (few are still alive), the women who have replaced the departed *shnorrers* in remodeled, rebuilt houses, look over the fruit and vegetables (ironically like Bibul's old rejects and reduced-to-clears because of prior though elegant pawing), buy a little, haggle not at all, or withdraw with a snub at peddling, a bow in favor of the superior refrigeration of supermarkets.

Through the streets where old Malkeh drew that creaking wagon, urged on by leather-capped Bibul, chrome-trimmed cars speed in unending gaggle, their sport-capped, stylishly hatted drivers in control of power the equivalent of four hundred un-Malkeh horses. The mayor tells Winnipeggers to "Think Big", bid for the Pan-American Games, hang out more flags and buntings. Slums like Bibul's "island" and the City Hall are fortunately doomed; Winnipeg is obviously a better place to live in.

Who doesn't welcome prosperity?

But the fact remains: I cannot find Bibul's like in Winnipeg today.

And that is why here and now, in this, his and my city, I write you this requiem for Bibul, for his face, for his Great Cause, his tic, his wave, his *aaaa*. In love and the joy of remembering I sing you this Bibul and all that's past and passing but not to come.

When the City Hall is torn down they will build Winnipeg a new one; but where, O where shall we find more Bibuls?

I THINK YOU ARE A WHOLE CITY
Earle Birney

i think you are a whole city

& yesterday when i first touched
you i started moving
thru one of your suburbs
where all the gardens are fresh
with faces of you
flowering up

some girls are only houses
maybe a strip
development
woman you are miles
of boulevards with supple trees
unpruned & full of winding
honesties

so give me time   i want
i want to know
all your squares & cloverleafs
im steering now by a constellation
winking over this nights rim
from some great beachside of you
with highrisers & a spotlit
beaux arts

i can hear your beat-
ing center   will i
will i make it
are there maps of you
i keep circling   imagining
parks fountains   your stores

back in my single bed i wander
your stranger   dreaming
i am your citizen

TORONTO
THE GOLDEN-VAULTED CITY

Miriam Waddington

I'm in a rich cold city,
Toronto the golden-vaulted,
runnelled and hollowed,
British born, steeped by cliffs,
axed by watercourses,
its warehouses pure Ontario,
its lake like Michigan,
and all its warm bungalows
lighted with midwinter's
scarcity of snow.

Alas poor York;
the howling wind outside
shakes the grey plateau,
stalks the gothic arches
in the dark moist marketplace,
follows under the overpass,
pursues like Caligari
in subway alleys
where the white-tiled breath
of unearthly cold
foretastes the sooty grave.

Dragon-tall is my adversary;
from arctic cold he rises,
but I am murdered, bloodless
in the untenanted subdivision
among the broken bricks
and chickenwire debris
I'm dry as last year's berries
under the frozen hedge.

The moundbuilders are dead
in my native province,
the grain elevators

are locked on the lakehead,
and the vaulted city blazes
like a many-pronged golden
pitchfork stabbing the clouds
for light

WINNIPEG SEEN AS A BODY OF TIME AND SPACE
James Reaney

Winnipeg, what once were you. You were,
Your hair was grass by the river ten feet tall,
Your arms were burr oaks and ash leaf maples,
Your backbone was a crooked silver muddy river,
Your thoughts were ravens in flocks, your bones were snow,
Your legs were trails and your blood was a people
      Who did what the stars did and the sun.

Then what were you? You were cracked enamel like
Into parishes and strips that come down to the river.
Convents were built, the river lined with nuns
Praying and windmills turning and your people
Had a blood that did what a star did and a Son.

Then on top of you fell
A Boneyard wrecked auto gent, his hair
Made of rusted car door handles, his fingernails
Of red Snowflake Pastry signs, his belly
Of buildings downtown; his arms of sewers,
His nerves electric wires, his mouth a telephone,
His backbone — a cracked cement street. His heart
An orange pendulum bus crawling with the human fleas
Of a so-so civilization — half gadget, half flesh —
      I don't know what I would have instead —
      And they did what they did more or less.

VANCOUVER I
Frank Davey

I watch the workmen
take the steel braces
from between the frail concrete
of a new building,
while next door
an old redbrick one
is battered into slag
and burnt.

Years ago there was a tent here
— you see the pictures in the Centennial Guide —
then the campfire ashes
were kicked aside
and frame and clapboard
— still scented with the breath
of first-seen timber —
hammered together.

Later
grey stone brought in from somewhere east
shining bricks
                from Clayburn
— short years of barter
bringing it about
short years of human eyes
regarding one strip
of sterile dirt.

        In the mountains you can see
        the ghost
        the ghostly towns abound:
        Huntingdon
                        a skeleton of noble streets,
        Barkerville
                        a green-hung

          grey-board mummy
Fairview
                    some grassed-in ashes
          phoenix moved on.

But here
the ashes are made
and hurried away,
by generations of men
whose children
fight to build castles
daily in the sand.

THE SAGA OF THE FINE-TOOTHED COMB
James H. Gray

Machray school where I was enrolled in 1913 was far from being a slum district school, yet its population was almost as cosmopolitan as any. Mountain Avenue was a sort of borderland between the congested new Canadian settlements to the south and the predominantly Anglo-Saxon district to the north. But the former was steadily expanding northward by sheer force of numbers. Thus many families that had moved out of the ghetto to more comfortable quarters often gave shelter to relatives or friends newly arrived from the old country. So there was a steady infusion of immigrant children into Machray school. My own experience illustrates the situation. My transfer from Norwood school was issued with the space for the name of the new school left blank. I took it to Strathcona school near Stella and Salter and was accommodated there for a couple of months. But so great was the crush of new immigrant pupils into Strathcona that I was shifted to Machray, which was somewhat closer to our home on Salter Street.

The Strathcona school year was a towerless Babel and during my short attendance I often felt completely out of place because I spoke no language but English. It was different, and a lot more comfortable, at Machray, where English predominated. Both schools, however, wrestled with the problem of beginning children who came into class without a word of English to their names. By this time the teachers had worked out a rough-and-ready system of handling the problem.

They would seat the children who could speak some English next to those who could speak none so that work could proceed with one translating for the other. Within a matter of weeks, even days sometimes, the children caught on so quickly that translation could be dispensed with. Once compulsory school attendance became law in 1916, however, it brought such an influx into the school system of pupils who could speak no English that this method would no longer work. There were rooms in Strathcona school, for example, where scarcely a child understood more than a dozen or so words of English. The teachers there solved their instructional dilemma by a combination of signs, sounds, and gestures. The day might begin with three words, "take out book", repeated slowly by the teacher several times. Then the class would repeat each word with pantomimic action. Then the sounds went onto the blackboard and letters were made in scribblers.

In the schoolyards the kids tended at first to cluster together in national groups and to use their native languages. That once led to an agitation by the super patriots that a regulation be enforced requiring only English to be spoken in the schoolyards. However, some sort of centrifugal force operated to spin the children out of their national groups into conglomerates. The most potent force was the playing of schoolyard games. A couple of Polish girls might have some qualms about inviting a Jewish girl into their skipping game. But rope-turners were always needed, so they handed her one end of the rope and she was in. With the boys, who tended more toward team sports, rounding up a couple of soccer teams or baseball teams required the participation of every boy in the room. Left to their own devices, the small fry tended to use their own languages at the games. But there were usually enough English-speaking children around to dominate the shouting. While all the other children learned English, the only foreign words we ever learned were the swear words.

Of all the immigrant groups the swear words of the Ukrainians were probably the most earthy. For years and years a Ukrainian bookstore on North Main Street exhibited a huge print in its window of a famous painting by a Russian master. It was entitled "The Cossacks' Reply to the Czar". It showed a group of rowdy Cossack soldiers gathered around a table at which one of their number was writing down insults dictated by the others. The soldiers were laughing uproariously at their epistle, which ran to several pages. A Ukrainian acquaintance once said that many of the insults were readable, upside down, in the original, but the print maker had opaqued the writing to make it indecipherable to the more prudish eyes of modern Ukrainians. When the small fry got angry at their games, which was frequently, most of them turned to their homey native oaths to express their displeasure. The English language was vastly inferior when it came to name-calling, so we all picked up their oaths and added them to our vocabulary.

Once, when we lived on Mountain Avenue, I had gotten into a row with a couple of Ukrainian kids who chased me home crying. When I reached the safety of my yard I turned and let fly a string of swear words I had accumulated. My mother heard the ruckus and came out to investigate just as a Ukrainian woman was passing.

"Missus," she said, "Missus know what boy say?"

My mother shook her head. "He say so bad words." She held her hand over her mouth. "Oh so bad words." Then she beckoned to my mother and whispered a rough translation of what I had said. My horrified mother caught me by the back of the neck and lathered me up the steps and into the house. All the time she was threatening to tell my father when he came home. She never did, largely, I suspect, because she couldn't bring herself to repeat the translation even in a whisper to my father. It was, as I later discovered, an all-encompassing, mouth-filling oath that ran the gamut from bestiality through incest to rape and was usually the last insult hurled before the fight started.

Every nationality delighted in the ancient game of teaching the *auslander* swear words for articles of common usage. In this game we came out far ahead because the foreign kids were much more eager to learn our language than we were to learn theirs. Eventually they learned the danger of asking any of us Anglo-Saxons, "Please, how do you say 'drink'?"

It was a common occurrence for a shy little immigrant child to raise her hand in school to ask to leave the room and use one of our four-letter words for something entirely different. That set off a storm of laughter which made the day for the Anglo-Saxons in the room. I have always suspected that the practice of identifying desired purposes by holding up one, two, or three fingers derived from such earthy language difficulties.

The language problem was by no means as acute at Machray school as it was at Norquay and Strathcona. If I had been in

Grade Three or Four when I came to Winnipeg I might never have known it existed. By that time English was the language of communication among the various ethnic groupings. But I started school in Grade One, which was where all the new immigrants in the neighbourhood started regardless of age unless they could speak English. Naturally, as quickly as they picked up the language they moved into the appropriate peer group. But in the beginning our Grade One at Machray struggled with the same problems that occurred in Strathcona and the other melting-pot schools.

Winnipeg, no less than Canada itself, owes its existence in large measure to Sir Clifford Sifton's immigration policies. No Canadian history ignores this policy or fails to mention the hundreds of thousands of settlers who came to Canada as the direct result of it. But my generation knew nothing of Sifton or policies of immigration. We knew only the end result of his policy as it was personified by a funny-looking little immigrant boy standing by the edge of the Norquay schoolyard watching the rest of us play soccer, and wanting passionately to participate. Or as it was illustrated by a little immigrant girl in the beginners' class at Machray school, reaching up to scratch her head and triggering a class uproar.

"Anna," the teacher would call sharply, putting her work to one side and reaching into the middle drawer of her desk, "come up here, please."

There was always a short pause while the teacher zeroed in on which of the half-dozen Annas in the class she wanted. When that was sorted out the little girl would usually burst into tears before getting to her feet. Sometimes the teacher had to come and take her by the arm. There were even times when more physical force than a girl teacher could muster was needed to move the pupil out of her seat. Then the teacher would appeal to one of the other children to explain to the little girl in her own language what was involved and what had to be done. For some reason or other, it always seemed to take two other little girls, both talking at once in Ukrainian, Polish, German, or Yiddish, to quiet the object of the teacher's attention and get her to co-operate.

What was involved was a hair-combing with a fine-toothed comb, in search of lice in the hair of the pupil. The teacher knew from experience that when any pupil started scratching at a real insect it would not be long before half the room would be scratching away at imaginary itches. So Anna took her place beside the teacher's desk while the teacher ran her comb through the pupil's hair in long, slow strokes. At Machray school our teacher was Miss Horn, who kept a newspaper in a bottom drawer. This she spread out over the desk, and leaned the pupil's head over the centre of the sheet so that the lice that failed to adhere to the comb dropped onto the paper, to be squashed with an inkwell. When the combing was finished the pupil returned to her seat and the room went back to work. Our first brush with public school delousing at the beginning of the term was an exciting event and we all watched goggle-eyed. A girl in the front row near the teacher's desk squealed excitedly, "There it is, Miss Horn! There it is! I saw it drop on the paper, right there."

So there was a lot of neck-craning and some of us even left our seats. As the weeks passed the lice hunt eventually lost its zest and we ignored it and went on with whatever we were doing while the operation was being performed. Or perhaps the homes of the immigrant children became less infested, and less public combing was needed. Certainly a fine-toothed comb was standard equipment in all the North End homes, for lice were no less endemic in the overcrowded immigrant homes than they were in the schools.

The regular North End school teachers quickly learned to cope with the scratching problem. There were other problems that took longer. The worst thing that could happen to a little immigrant boy was to make a winter entry into the public school system and bump into a substitute teacher with un-realistic ideas about neatness. Our standard winter footwear was a pair of moccasins or shoepacks with two or three pairs of socks. Immigrant children, however, often wore knee-length heavy felt mukluks to which rubbers were permanently at-

tached at the bottom. Some of them kept slippers in their
pockets and in school they'd take off the mukluks and wear
the slippers. But many of the newcomers had the tops of their
mukluks stitched to the bottoms of their pant legs just below
the knees. When these kids started clumping around the
room, a new teacher would instruct them to go into the
clothes lobby and take off their rubbers. Impossible. If the
rubbers came off, so did the mukluks and so did the pants!
Most regular teachers understood all this and learned to sur-
vive in rooms reeking with the smell of mukluks drying out.
But every now and then a teacher from south Winnipeg would
turn up. It would take the class half the morning to get her
straightened out about the facts of daily life in the North End
of Winnipeg.

Teachers were easily shaken down, but I have often wondered since what effect the first few months in Canadian
schools had on the personalities of the immigrant children. It
was hard enough for an Anglo-Saxon like me, who knew the
language, to move only from one school to another. Each
move always entailed a couple of split lips and bloody noses
before I settled into my place in the schoolyard pecking order.
How much more painful, terrifying even, it must have been
for the newcomers to be pitchforked into such an environment,
where the natives were unfriendly and the language was impossible. It must have been humiliating in the extreme for a
shy and sensitive seven-year-old to be summoned forward, by a
teacher she feared, to have her hair combed, often ungently,
by a sharp-toothed instrument that dug at the scalp or got
snagged on knots. And it must have been cold comfort to discover later that the combing ordeal was one that everyone in
the room would undergo eventually, for such was the way of
the migrant lice in the cloakrooms of the North End schools.
But painful though the experiences were at the time, I doubt
that they did much permanent harm to the psyches of the new
Canadians. For one thing, they were a lot stronger and
tougher physically than we were. For another, they had already
come halfway round the world and survived a hundred shocks

and surprises, not the least of which was an interminable ocean voyage followed by an interminable railway journey. Mere teachers they could take in their stride, and if not, they could work off their frustrations beating up the Anglo-Saxon kids in the neighbourhood. They did.

I have often wondered how much of the prejudice that developed in Winnipeg against the whole immigrant population germinated in what could be called the fine-toothed-comb syndrome. For many Anglo-Saxon families, it was the first intimate contact they had with the immigrant world, and to use my mother's word, a "disgusting" one it was. It was not that the average Anglo-Saxon was any more fastidious than the average Ukrainian or Jewish family. Nor did the immigrant kids have a monopoly on transporting lice to school. At this stage, however, the Anglo-Saxons were firmly established several rungs further up the economic ladder than the immigrants. Hence they were not hived off in enclaves crowded with lice-infested rooming houses in the older parts of the city. The English, Scottish, and Irish immigrants, moreover, were not driven to congregate together because they could not speak the language of the country. They were thus able to spread out a little more, in cottages clustering around the C.P.R. shops in Weston, for example. If they lived in North Winnipeg, however, there was no way in which they could isolate themselves from the lice if they had children in school.

Even in the best homes in North Winnipeg, as in the district's better schools, the scratching of a young head evoked an automatic response. Out came the fine-toothed comb. When the lice were extracted they were dispatched simply by squashing between thumb-nails or, for the more squeamish, by drowning in coal oil or by burning.

"There! That must be all of them," an impatient mother would sigh. "Now for goodness' sake stay away from those hunky kids because I am sick and tired of combing bugs out of your hair!"

Where parents harboured no original prejudices against the immigrants, the repetition of hair-combing incidents was well

112

designed to create them. They were certainly prejudiced against lice; "hunky" kids and lice went together. The fact that there were immigrant families who were as finicky about bugs as they were probably never occurred to them. Their responses were as automatic as those of Pavlov's dogs. Scratching signified lice, which produced the fine-toothed comb and the combination spelled hunky.

It would, however, be unwise to blame too much of the prejudice on lice. Adult Winnipeg of the era was as race-proud, bigoted, and prejudice-driven as any city on earth. The Ukrainians, Poles, and Jews who had come to Canada to escape from the Czar's military conscription did not rush madly to join the Canadian army when war broke out. Indeed, the only big rush was by the recently arrived British immigrants, many of whom saw the war as a free ride home for a visit, as something that would be over long before it involved them. When that illusion was shattered, and recruiting fell off, the aliens became a target for everyone. If an Anglo-Saxon wanted a job that some immigrant had, he thought nothing of demanding it as his right and insisting that the immigrant be fired. When labour troubles developed, they were blamed on alien agitators. The deportation of aliens was demanded by newspapers, labour leaders, preachers, and politicians with varying degrees of intensity.

Winnipeg prejudice, moreover, was not something about which simple generalizations were possible. Within the prejudices of each of the general categories of people were a lot of subsidiary ones. My father, for example, thoroughly disliked all Englishmen. How much of this went back to his days in anti-British Buffalo, and how much was new growth from the fact that the English dominated the civil service in Manitoba, is problematic. Whenever he failed in an attempt for some sort of clerical job in the civil service, his explanation was always the same: "They gave it to a bloody Englishman!"

There may have been a shadow of substance to his reasoning. All the immigrant groups quickly developed mutual aid associations, formal or informal. Getting a start in the new world was hard enough for any of the newcomers. When one got a job, he naturally looked around for a job for his wife's brother or the cousin of a Liverpool, Manchester, or London neighbour. There were not only English, Irish, and Scottish fraternal societies running full blast, there were secret societies and trade unions in which they could work for mutual advancement. A circumspect immigrant from Glasgow could certainly improve his chances if he were a Royal Arch Mason of the Scottish Rite, a member of the Sons of Scotland or the Knights of Pythias, a Knight Templar, and a supporter of the Dunfermline, Dundee, and Strathroy Association. Even the religious denominations tended to become mutual assistance societies, functioning to exclude those they disliked from gainful employment. It was curious how one catch-phrase was used by so many diverse groups: "Let one of them in and they'll take over the place."

The Presbyterians used it against the Catholics, the Catholics used it against the Jews. The Irish and English used it against the Scots and all the Anglo-Saxons used it against all the aliens.

But this was in the adult world. In ours, we also chose up sides racially and nationally, perhaps with the herd instinct operating in the interest of self-preservation. If a couple of Irish, English, Jewish, or Polish kids got into a fight with each other, the rest of us tended to stand back and let them go at it. We confined our participation to shouting encouragement to the one we favoured. But if a Jewish kid tangled with a Polish kid, it was not long before several other Jewish-Polish fights were going on, or two or three of one group would gang up on one of the other. We learned quickly, in the North End, always to make a quick nose count of the odds before letting the first fist fly. But in our vocal world, as distinct from our physical world, we tended to use all the labels without cluttering them with odious connotations. "Hunky" was a generic term that included all aliens of whatever national origin or religious persuasion. If we didn't know the name of a boy we were trying to identify we would

114

refer to him as "the hunky kid who lives down the lane in that brown house".

Whether the process was helped by referring to him as a "hunky kid" never caused us any concern. It was a word we used when a better one did not come readily to mind. When we wanted to differentiate more sharply, we might refer to him as the "Polack kid", or the "Uke kid", or the "Jew kid". It was only when we got mad and started bandying insults that we used words that were intended to cut and slice — words like "bohunk" or "kike" or "wop" — and these usually were coupled with "dirty" for better effect. All these words, it should be emphasized, were words that got into our vocabulary in the schoolyards and were not consciously selected to define social attitudes. What the foreign kids called us we never really knew because, as I have said, they reached into the language underground of their own tongue for suitable epithets.

The plain truth was that many an Anglo-Saxon kid spent much of his life envying the foreign kids. The Jews, for example, always seemed to be getting off on special holidays of their own while we had to stay in school and work. Not only did the Ukrainian kids have our Christmas holidays, they had a week in January when they had Christmas all over again. Even the Catholics who were not foreigners got away with murder, in our judgment. They had saints' days and feast days which gave them extra time away from school. There was even a custom then of honouring St. Patrick's Day, St. George's Day, and Burns' Day with special entertainment in the schools. Except for Victoria Day, the only day Canadian kids had anything to celebrate was the First of July and that was a holiday anyway.

There was undoubtedly a great deal of anti-Semitism in the North End of Winnipeg, and some of the parental attitudes must have filtered down to the children. Certainly the Poles and the Jews kept their distance from each other and the Ukrainians brought with them when they came their prejudice against both. For us, however, "Jew" was just another generic word that often included the peddlers who were Italian or Greek. When we scrounged bottles and scrap metal it was to sell to "the Jew", who was anybody that came along buying junk. The word "Jew" was also a verb that was synonymous for "bargain vigorously". If we haggled successfully over something we would say, "I Jewed him down."

I was well on in school, indeed, before I discovered that the Jews did not celebrate Christmas like the rest of us. We were living in the Rozell Apartments on Clark Street by then. A Jewish family lived on the third floor and their boy Izzy was in my brother's room at school. On Christmas morning I was overjoyed with my present — a pair of C.C.M. Automobile D skates which were screwed to my summer boots. My brothers each got a sleigh and my father bought a table gramophone for my mother. It came with half a dozen records. Four of them were Christmas hymns; one was "Carry Me Back to Blighty" and the other was a comic recitation entitled "The Preacher and the Bear".

After we had taken turns winding the gramophone and had squeezed as much laughter as possible out of it, I wanted to try out my skates. So I went to see if Izzy wanted to go skating with me. He had also got some new skates and I brought him down to see our new gramophone and listen to "The Preacher and the Bear". He wanted to listen to our other records so I put them on one after the other. He liked "Hark! the Herald Angels Sing" and "Adeste, Fideles". He kept time with those by pretending he was playing the piano and whistling. We played them a couple of times. Then he asked my mother if he could borrow the two records to play on his gramophone and see if he could follow them on the piano. It didn't come off. He would get going nicely and then hit a couple of wrong keys while the gramophone music got away and he could never catch up. It never occurred to me then, or even much later, that his was the only kosher household in Winnipeg from which Christmas carols could be heard emanating that morning.

QUESTIONS ON THE THEME:
The Urban Experience

1. Even in a crowded city loneliness can take many forms. How would you describe the various states of loneliness in "The Saga of the Fine-toothed Comb", "Fog", and "On Saint-Urbain Street"? What other selections in this book convey a sense of loneliness?

2. What would you say are some of the differences in the authors' attitudes toward remembered childhood in "Autobiographical", "The Saga of the Fine-toothed Comb", and "The Great Electrical Revolution"?

3. In one of his sketches, "The Hidden Secret of the City", Stephen Leacock says, "The Great City! There's no such place. It's just where people go, bravely enough, to earn the money to get back home." Do you think his statement applies to any of the people you know who have moved to the city from smaller communities? Test the validity of Leacock's generalization by applying it to any of the selections in *The Urban Experience*.

4. What is your understanding of the term *satire*?
Which of the poems or prose pieces in this collection could be called satires?
What follies or weaknesses in urban life does each satirize?
Which selections are most effective as satires? Why?

5. Some of the writers in this book speak about contemporary urban life (for example: Margaret Atwood, Heather Robertson, Lionel Kearns, Hugh Garner, P. K. Page, Frank Davey, Katherine McGillivray, Hugh Hood), while others deal with urban life in earlier generations (Lawren Harris, Alexander McLachlan, James Gray, Archibald Lampman, Pierre Vallières, Jack Ludwig). Judging from the accounts of these writers, what elements of city life seem much the same today as they were in earlier years? What differences can you detect?

6. Lyric poems tend either to celebrate some aspect of experience or to lament it. Which of the poems chosen for this book seem

117

predominantly to celebrate city life? Which seem to lament it? If you were to write a poem about the city you know best, which of the two polarities, celebration or lament, would you favour? Try expressing one of your city experiences in a poem. (If you wish to turn lament into laughter, you might try a satiric poem.)

7. Every short story implies a comment on life, a comment that is sometimes called the theme of the story. If the central character is attractive to us and experiences some kind of victory, then we feel that what the story implies about life is that it carries this possibility of purpose and the triumph of good. If, on the other hand, the central character is likeable, yet still fails miserably in his endeavour, then we feel that the implied comment on life is that such failure is the common fate of man. Stories, like poems, tend either to celebrate the joy of life or to lament its pain.
What celebrations or laments concerning urban life are suggested by the various stories in this collection?
Pick out a moment in each story which for you most powerfully implies the writer's comment on life.

8. In the non-fiction prose of *The Urban Experience* the writers offer *direct* criticisms of urban life. Which of the pieces would you say carries the strongest social criticism?
Which seems to be the most emotionally detached and objective?
Which piece of non-fiction writing did you like best? Why?

9. The typical urban environment today provides an example of the most sophisticated network of communications and travel that mankind has ever known. And yet in every big city thousands of people are unable to communicate adequately with others about their basic emotional problems. What evidence of this condition can you find expressed in the prose and poetry of *The Urban Experience*?
Which selections suggest an optimistic solution to the problem?

BIBLIOGRAPHY

BIOGRAPHICAL INFORMATION

Carl F. Klinck, *A Literary History of Canada: Canadian Literature in English*, University of Toronto Press

Norah Story, *The Oxford Companion to Canadian History and Literature*, Oxford University Press

William Stewart Wallace, *The Macmillan Dictionary of Canadian Biography*, Macmillan of Canada

NOVELS

Margaret Atwood, *The Edible Woman*, New Canadian Library

Constance Beresford-Howe, *The Book of Eve*, Macmillan of Canada

Morley Callaghan, *The Loved and the Lost*, Laurentian Library; *More Joy in Heaven*, New Canadian Library; *Such Is My Beloved*, New Canadian Library

Roch Carrier, *Is It the Sun, Philibert?*, Anansi; *They Won't Demolish Me*, Anansi

Selwyn Dewdney, *Wind without Rain*, New Canadian Library

Hugh Garner, *Cabbagetown*, Pocket Book; *Silence on the Shore*, Pocket Book

André Langevin, *Dust Over the City*, New Canadian Library

Margaret Laurence, *The Fire Dwellers*, New Canadian Library

John Marlyn, *Under the Ribs of Death*, New Canadian Library

Hugh MacLennan, *Two Solitudes*, Laurentian Library; *Barometer Rising*, Macmillan of Canada; *Return of the Sphinx*, Laurentian Library

Brian Moore, *The Luck of Ginger Coffey*, New Canadian Library

Mordecai Richler, *Son of a Smaller Hero*, New Canadian Library; *The Apprenticeship of Duddy Kravitz*, Penguin

Gabrielle Roy, *The Cashier*, New Canadian Library; *The Tin Flute*, New Canadian Library; *Street of Riches*, New Canadian Library

Adele Wiseman, *The Sacrifice*, Laurentian Library

Richard Wright, *The Weekend Man*, Macmillan of Canada

PLAYS

Carol Bolt, *Buffalo Jump*, Playwrights' Co-op

David French, *Leaving Home,* New Press; *Of the Fields Lately,* New Press

Gratien Gélinas, *Bousille and the Just,* Clarke, Irwin; *Yesterday the Children Were Dancing,* Clarke, Irwin

Harvey Markowitz, *Branch Plant,* Playwrights' Co-op

J. T. McDonough, *Charbonneau and Le Chef,* McClelland and Stewart (radio adaptation available on 2 LP discs, Recordings from CBC Learning Systems)

George Ryga, *The Ecstasy of Rita Joe,* Talonbooks

Norman Williams, *He Didn't Even Say Goodbye,* Playwrights' Co-op

FEATURE FILMS.

Don't Let the Angels Fall, black and white, 98 minutes, National Film Board. Distributor: Columbia Pictures

Goin' Down the Road, colour, 88 minutes, Don Shebib. Distributor: New Cinema Enterprises

Nobody Waved Goodbye, black and white, 80 minutes, National Film Board. Distributor: Columbia Pictures

The Ernie Game, black and white, 88 minutes, National Film Board. Distributor: Columbia Pictures

SHORT FILMS

All the films listed below are from the 1974 catalogue of the National Film Board of Canada.

A Matter of Survival, black and white, 25 minutes

Autobiographical by A. M. Klein, black and white, 10 minutes

Beyond Kicks, colour, 28 minutes

Boomsville, colour, cartoon animation, 10 minutes

Day after Day, black and white, 27 minutes

High Steel, colour, 14 minutes

Legault's Place, black and white, 10 minutes

Paul Tomkowicz: Street-railway Switchman, black and white, 9 minutes

120

Strike in Town, black and white, 29 minutes
The City and the Future, black and white, 28 minutes
The Persistent Seed, colour, 14 minutes
The Purse, black and white, 11 minutes
The Quiet Racket, colour, 7 minutes
The Red Kite, colour, 17 minutes
The Summer We Moved to Elm Street, colour, 28 minutes
Trafficopter, colour, 10 minutes
23 Skidoo, black and white, 8 minutes
21-87, black and white, 9 minutes
What on Earth?, colour animation, 10 minutes
Note: For an annotated catalogue of all available NFB films, write
to the nearest regional office of the National Film Board of
Canada.

RECORDINGS

Cabbagetown and Don Mills, audiotape, 30 minutes, CBC Learning
Systems
John Drainie Reads Stephen Leacock, disc, Melbourne, SMLP, 4015
The Canadian City Seen Through the Eyes of the Poet, audiotape, 60
minutes, CBC Learning Systems
The Urban Spaceship, audiotape, 30 minutes, CBC Learning Systems
What Is a City?, audiotape, 30 minutes, CBC Learning Systems
Note: For an annotated catalogue of all available CBC publica-
tions and recordings, write to: CBC Learning Systems, Box
500, Terminal A, Toronto, Ontario, M5W 1E6.

57   67   77   87   97   08   18   28   38   T.H.B.   9   8   7   6   5   4   3   2   1